22 favourite songs in English, French and Spanish.

Piano arrangements and musical scoring by Bob Wishinski

Illustrations & photography by Leslie Ash
Graphics by giga'graphics inc.

No matter what age we are, we all need the happiness that music can bring into our lives. Everyday seems a little bit brighter when it begins with a song and ends with a soothing melody and a good story. I hope that this songbook brings a smile to your face and leaves you with a song in your heart. Don't forget that "Four Hugs a Day" keep the blues away!

I would like to dedicate this book to my family, my husband, Harry and my sons, Matt and Tom. Without their support, understanding and gentle criticism, my music would never have taken wing. Thanks for keeping me flying!

I would also like to thank my parents, Stewart and Helen Houston, for encouraging me from childhood to express myself and communicate my ideas; the Hug Bug Band, Paul Gitlitz (my producer), Bob Wishinski, David Jonsson, Dennis Nichol and Lee Oliphant, who are all responsible for bringing my songs alive on stage and in the studio; a special Thank You to Rita Noon for being such a wonderful administrator of Hug Bug Music, to Dan Noon for turning my songs into exciting, innovative videos and to Monica and Stephanie for their help. Last of all to Diane and Shirley Tokheim, Dennis and Linda Ronberg, Chauni Haslet, Phyllis Simon, Shirley Handy, Ronnie Silverstone, Jackie Thompson and all the wonderful teachers who gave me great ideas along the way. I am indebted to you all!

ISBN 0-9681999-2-5

All inquiries should be addressed to:
Hug Bug Music Inc.
6251 Chatsworth Road, Richmond, B.C. Canada V7C 3S4
(604) 274-8216 Fax: (604) 274-8210
E-mail: hugbug@intergate.bc.ca

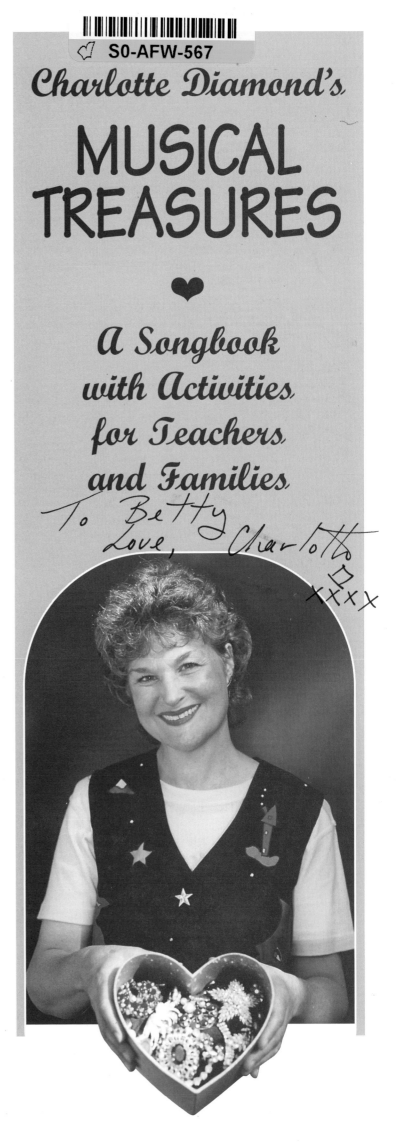

S0-AFW-567

Charlotte Diamond's
MUSICAL TREASURES

♥

A Songbook with Activities for Teachers and Families

To Betty
Love, Charlotte
xxxx

Award-Winning Recordings and Videos by Charlotte Diamond

10 Carrot Diamond
- CD & cassette   ☆ **Juno Award, Parents' Choice Classic Award, American Library Award**
- with Octopus, Four Hugs a Day, I am a Pizza & Each of Us Is a Flower.

Diamond in the Rough
- CD & cassette
- Songs for self-esteem and songs about family life - with The Hug Bug, Metamorphosis, The Days of the Week, You Never Praise Me Enough, Donne-moi la main (Give Me Your Hand) & The Laundry!

Qu'il y ait toujours le soleil
- cassette
- Charlotte's favourites in French - Je suis une pizza, La belle pieuvre, La Bastringue et Tout ce que je veux - la Paix

Diamonds and Dragons
- CD & cassette   ☆ **Parent's Choice Honors Award**
- with Dicky Dinosaur, Slimy the Slug, Lucky Streak & You Can Make a Miracle

The Christmas Gift
- CD & Cassette   ☆ **American Library Award**
- Holiday Favourites from around the world - with The Zulu Carol, Silver Bells & Feliz Navidad

My Bear Gruff
- CD & cassette   ☆ **Parents' Choice Gold Award**
- with Listen to the Water, All the Nations Like Banana, Puddles, It's a Rainy Day & My Bear Gruff!

Bonjour l'hiver
- cassette
- Favourite holiday & winter songs in French - Side B has the instrumental accompaniment for performance. with Vive le Vent, L'enfant au tambour, Sainte Nuit & Bonjour l'hiver.

Soy una Pizza
- CD & cassette   ☆ **American Library Award & NAPPA Award**
- Charlotte's hit songs in Spanish with Cuatro abrazos al diá (Four Hugs a Day), De Colores, Di, Dinosaurio (Dicky Dinosaur), La Bamba, and Un pulpito (Octopus)

Sing Along With Charlotte Diamond
- cassette
- Old Time Favourites for all the Family. with Bicycle Built for Two, I've Been Working on the Railroad & Red River Valley
- Also available in Video - great for Senior's Sing Alongs

Diamonds and Daydreams
- CD & cassette   ☆ **Parents' Choice Seal of Approval & NAPPA Award**
- This musical adventure is a treat for the whole family. 18 thoughtful and singable songs that inspire imagination and creativity with My Favourite Things, Morningtown Ride, Everyday Angel, One Dream, Roots and Wings and Grandma's Eyes

VIDEOS

Diamond and Dragons
- Taped on location around Vancouver with the Hug Bug Band
- 10 songs - with Slimy the Slug, Dicky Dinosaur, The Laundry, La Bamba and The Hug Bug

10 Crunchy Carrots
- Award winning T.V. special based on 10 Carrot Diamond - with Sasquatch, I Wanna be a Dog, Octopus, I am a Pizza & Four Hugs a Day

To Order: call Hug Bug Music (604) 931-7375, fax (604) 931-2727

TABLE OF CONTENTS

(Fr, Sp & Eng) indicates that lyrics in French, Spanish or English are included.

FOUR HUGS A DAY

By: Earl Robinson/Charlotte Diamond

Credits: By Earl Robinson ASCAP and Charlotte Diamond SOCAN 1984
© Charlotte Diamond Music
As recorded on "10 Carrot Diamond"

Four Hugs a day,   that's the **minimum**   Four Hugs a day,   not the **maximum**.

Step One, look them right in the eye   Step Two, nose to nose   Step Three, reach your arms   Step Four, you can't do any harm with.

EMBRASSE QUATRE FOIS

French version by Charlotte Diamond 1985 SOCAN
As recorded on "Qu'il y ait toujours le soleil"

Il faut embrasser quatre fois par jour
Quatre c'est le minimum
Mais tu peux embrasser plus souvent
'Y a pas de maximum.

Refrain
Embrasse quatre fois, c'est le minimum
Quatre fois, ce n'est pas le maximum   (bis)

1.
Premier pas, regarde dans les yeux
Deuxième pas, nez à nez
Troisième pas, étends les bras
Quatrième pas, embrasse doucement.
Refrain

2.
N'oublie pas ta maman et ton papa
Ta grand-mère, ton grand-père et tous tes amis
Ton frère et ta soeur, ta tante et ton oncle
Et tes professeurs aussi. Il faut...
Un, deux, trois et quatre, il faut...
Un, deux, trois et quatre.
Refrain

N'oublie pas, quatre fois par jour.

CUATRO ABRAZOS AL DÍA

Spanish version by Charlotte Diamond 1994 SOCAN
As recorded on "Soy una Pizza"

Necesitamos abrazar cuatro veces al día
Cuatro es el mínimo
Pero puedes abrazar más de cuatro veces
¡No es el máximo!

CORO
Abrázame, cuatro veces mínimo
Abrázame, no es el máximo   (bis)

1.
Paso uno, mirando a los ojos
Paso dos, cara a cara
Paso tres, abre los brazos
Paso cuatro, abraza con dulzor.
CORO

2.
No olvides tu mami ni tu papi
Tus abuelitos y amigos también
Hermanos y hermanas, tíos y tías
Sin olvidar tus maestros también.
Uno, dos, tres y cuatro
Uno, dos, tres y cuatro
CORO

¡Abracemos cuatro veces al día!

SAM.

DISCUSSION IDEAS

- When do you need a hug or a kind word to help you feel better? Did you hug your Mom or Dad or a favourite teddy bear today? Even our pets need a pat or a hug to keep them happy.

- Let's start by hugging and taking care of ourselves. Here's a way to give "Four Hugs".
  Number One - Hug your big toe,
  Number Two - Hug your nose,
  Number Three - Hug your hair,
  Number Four - Hug your tummy and
  Number Five - (because we need more than Four Hugs a Day)
  - Reach out your arms and give yourself a **Bear Hug**!

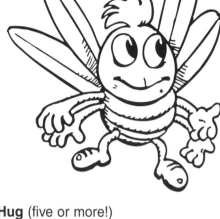

ACTIVITIES

- Learn the actions to the song and give a hug to a partner.

- Change the steps to: cheek to cheek, knee to knee, toe to toe . . . etc.

- Give a **Sandwich Hug** (three people), a **Pizza Hug** (four) or a **Monster Hug** (five or more!)
  This is a great way to learn multiplication and division. Fifteen people can be divided into five Sandwich Hugs. You can also use stuffed animals and teddy bears to count hugs.

- Count hugs in another language, such as, **French** - un, deux, trois et quatre,
  Spanish - uno, dos, tres y cuatro, or **German** - eins, zwei, drei, vier.

- Try singing the song in French, "Embrasse quatre fois" or Spanish, "Cuatro abrazos al día".
  The actions stay the same

- Make Hug Coupons that say "Good for one hug from _____ to_____."
  Start with four coupons each day, then give a card and a hug to your family and friends.

Sneak up on a buddy
and send the "I love you"
sign before they can!

DISCUSSION IDEAS

♥ There are many different moods in this song - feeling grumpy or sad, sniffling with a cold or hurt because you have fallen off of your bike. Talk about other situations when we need a hug or a kind word. Discuss how to be a good friend, a caring brother or sister. What does a Hug Bug look like? - six legs, 4 wings, 2 antennae, a smile... etc.

ACTIVITIES

♥ Act out the different moods of this song.

♥ Make a **Hug Bug Stick Puppet** from cut out hearts, pipe cleaners (for antennae) and a craft stick. (See illustration).

♥ You can also make a **Paper Bag Hug Bug**. Draw a face on a small lunch bag then stuff with tissues or paper towels and tie off the top. Attach six legs on the sides and four wings on the back; then attach coloured wool on top for hair. Tie a string to your Hug Bug so that it can hang in the classroom or over your bed. Remember that Hug Bugs live all over the world, and they come in many different shapes, sizes and colours. So use your imagination!

♥ Write some new verses.
"When your best friend moves away, you may feel sad and blue
Send them a Hug Bug and a letter, too. And ask them to write to you."

♥ Draw your own Hug Bug and send it to:

**Charlotte Diamond's Hug Bug Club,
P.O. Box 58067, Vancouver, B.C. Canada V6P 6C5
She will write back to you!**

Or send a Hug Bug to your grandma, grandpa or a special friend.

Hug Bug Cookies

1. Make your favourite cookie dough. (sugar cookies or ice box cookies) Using a heart-shaped cookie cutter, cut out three large hearts. One heart is the body and the other two are the wings for either side.

2. Press the hearts together and cut down the centre of each side heart to make four wings. (See illustration)

3. Bake your Hug Bugs. When they are cool, ice and decorate with black licorice for antennae and M&M's, candied fruit and raisins for the eyes, nose, mouth and wings.

Your Hug Bugs may be too cute to eat!

THE HUG BUG

By: Charlotte Diamond

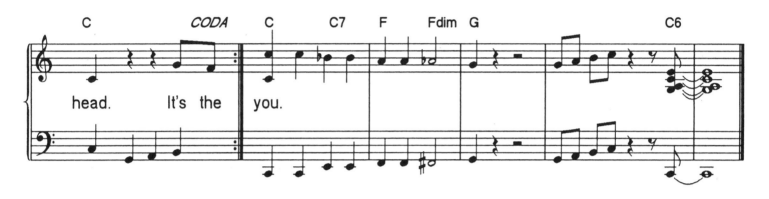

Credits: By Charlotte Diamond,
as recorded on "Diamond in the Rough"
© Charlotte Diamond Music 1985 SOCAN

(This song is recorded in the key of A)
CHORUS
The Hug Bug, the Hug Bug, the Hug Bug
Never know where it's hiding
It's the Hug Bug, the Hug Bug
Watch out it's gonna hug you!

1.
If you're in a growly mood
Sitting alone on your bed
The Hug Bug will sneak up from behind
And hug you right on the head. **CHORUS**

2.
If you're sniffling with a cold
And chilly right down to your toes
The Hug Bug will sneak in the middle of the night
And hug you right on the nose. **CHORUS**

3.
If you've tumbled off your bike
And skinned both of your knees
The Hug Bug will sneak up when you're not looking
And give you a great big squeeze. **CHORUS**

4.
Now it doesn't bite, it doesn't sting
Or buzz like another bug
It eats good wishes and happy dreams
And turns them into love.

5.
So if you're feeling upside down
Or twisted all around
Just keep your eyes open wide
'Cause the Hug Bug's coming to town. **CHORUS**

BRACITOS
Spanish Version of "The Hug Bug"
By Charlotte Diamond 1994 SOCAN
© Charlotte Diamond Music Inc.

CORO
Bracitos, Bracitos, Bracitos
¿Quien sabe donde está?
Bracitos, Bracitos
¡Cuidado! te viene a abrazar.

1.
Si tú estás muy enojado
Solo y triste en tu pieza
Bracitos viene por detrás
Y te abraza la cabeza.   **CORO**

2.
Si tú estás muy resfriado
Y no te sientas feliz
Bracitos viene con cuidado
Y te abraza la nariz.   **CORO**

3.
Si caes de tu bicicleta
O te das un tropezón
Bracitos viene por sorpresa
Y te da un buen apretón.   **CORO**

4.
El no muerde ni tiene aguijón
Ni zumba como un abejón
Vive de sueños y de ilusiónes
Que los convierte en amor.

5.
Si sientes mucha confusión
Y tu no puedes pensar
Buscá en todas direcciónes
Bracitos está por llegar.   **CORO**

MY BEAR GRUFF

By: Charlotte Diamond

1. There is a bear who I know, he's not ve - ry hand - some, but I love him so, 'cause he's my Ted - dy and I call him "Gruff," he's not ve - ry hand - some, but he's hand - some e - nough.

Verses 1 to 4.

Verse 5.

Oh...

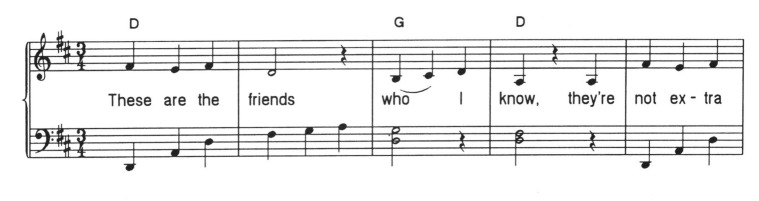

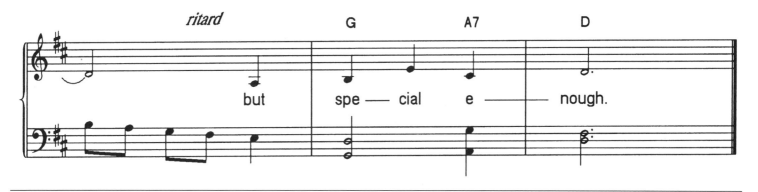

Credits: By Charlotte Diamond, as recorded on "My Bear Gruff"   © Charlotte Diamond Music 1991 SOCAN

1.
There is a bear who I know
He's not very handsome, but I love him so
'Cause he's my Teddy and I call him "Gruff"
He's not very handsome, but he's handsome enough.

2.
There is a kitty who I know
She's not very fluffy, but I love her so
'Cause she's my kitty and I call her "Puff"
She's not very fluffy, but she's fluffy enough.

3.
There is a dog who I know
He's not very young, but I love him so
'Cause he's my dog and I call him "Ruff"
He's not very young, but he's young enough.

4.
There is a rabbit who I know
She's not very big, but I love her so
'Cause she's my rabbit and I call her "Fluff"
She's not very big, but she's big enough.

5.
These are the friends who I know
They're not extra special, but I love them so
There's Gruff and Puff, Fluffy and Ruff
They're not extra special, but special enough!

MI OSO "GRUFF" (GRAFF)

Spanish version of "My Bear Gruff" By Charlotte Diamond SOCAN 1992
© Charlotte Diamond Music Inc.

1.
Hay un osito que conozco yo
Tal vez no es muy guapo pero le amo yo
Porque es mi osito y lo llamo "Gruff"
Tal vez no es tan guapo como lo veo yo.

2.
Hay un gatito que conozco yo
No es tan peludito pero le amo yo
Porque es mi gatito y lo llamo "Puff"
No es tan peludito como lo siento yo.

3.
Hay un perro que conozco yo
Tal vez no es muy joven pero le amo yo
Porque es mi perro y lo llamo "Ruff"
Tal vez no es tan joven como lo veo yo

4.
Hay un conejito que conozco yo
Tal vez no es tan grande pero le amo yo
Porque es mi conejito y lo llamo "Fluff"
Tal vez no es tan grande como lo veo yo.

5.
Son mis amigitos que conozco yo
No tan especiales pero los amo yo
Son "Gruff" y "Puff", "Fluff" y "Ruff"
No tan especiales como los veo yo.

*** "uff" is pronounced in Spanish as "aff"*

IDEAS & ACTIVITIES for MY BEAR GRUFF

DISCUSSION IDEAS

- Do you have a favourite teddy bear or stuffed animal? What do you like about this favourite friend? Will you love her even when she is old and tattered? No one is perfect, but we love each other for who we are. **"Bear Gruff"** is not very handsome but he's handsome enough. Good friendships can last forever.

- What are some qualities that make a good friend. (Sharing, caring when you are sad, waiting for you to catch up, listening, giving a hug, taking turns at play, smiling, lending a hand, just being there!) We are all different and this difference makes our world interesting. All our different talents allow us to help each other and to learn from each other.

- Do you have a pet? What does your pet need to be healthy and happy?

ACTIVITIES

- Divide into four groups. Each group takes turns singing a verse about the different animals Gruff, Puff, Ruff and Fluff. All groups sing the final verse with their arms around each other.

- Bring stuffed animals to class to act out the verses.

- Write new verses - a dragon called **"Tuff"**, a wolf called **"Huff"**, or a pig called **"Snuff"**.

- This song is in 3/4 or Waltz time. Waltz around the room to the music with a partner or with your favourite stuffed animal. Turn slowly in a circle.

- The Bear Gruff Dance - Join hands in a circle. Walk slowly toward the middle and then slowly back out while singing the song. (Four steps in, four steps out.) "Gruff" and his pals can be in the centre.
  - Walk forward: "There is a bear who I know"
  - Walk backward: "He's not very handsome, but I love him so"
  - Walk forward and raise hands: "He's my teddy and I call him Gruff"
  - Walk backward and lower hands: "He's not very handsome but handsome enough."

- Try different kinds of walks: Bear Walk, Kitty Stretch, Old Dog Walk and the Bunny Hop,

- Learn the song in Spanish. "Gruff" in English sounds like "Graff" in Spanish.

Other Animal Songs
"Animals Have Personality", "I Wanna Be a Dog", "Little Black Dog", "Mi Caramelita", "I Wanna a Purple Kitty for My Birthday, Mom", and the story - "The Imp with Blood-Red Eyes".

SASQUATCH (BIG FOOT)

By Charlotte Diamond, as recorded on "10 Carrot Diamond"
© Charlotte Diamond Music Inc. 1985 SOCAN

1.
Sasquatch (Sasquatch), won't you come on down
Sasquatch (Sasquatch), won't you come on down
Shed your furry coat and let the sun shine in
The door is open, come on in.

2.
Sasquatch (Sasquatch), we are just like you
Sasquatch (Sasquatch), we get frightened, too
Maybe you could learn to trust us as a friend
The door is open, come on in.

BRIDGE
When you're hiding in the mountains,
  so lonely and afraid
Hiding in the rocks and hiding in your cave
Growling at the world below in anger and in pain
And leaving great big footprints and the fear of
  your name!

Repeat verse 1
Sasquatch (Sasquatch), won't you come on down
Sasquatch (Sasquatch), won't you come on down
Shed your furry coat and let the sun shine in
The door is open, come on in

CODA
The door is open,
come on in
Sasquatch (Sasquatch),
Sasquatch (Sasquatch)
Sasquatch...

IDEAS & ACTIVITIES for SASQUATCH

DISCUSSION IDEAS

☞ Is Sasquatch real or imaginary? You may know "Sasquatch" by the name of "Big Foot" or "Yeti".
What does Sasquatch look like? What would you do if you saw a real Sasquatch?
We need to take care of the wild animals that share this earth with us. How can we help wildlife survive?

☞ What animals in your area are endangered and need our protection? What are some of the endangered animals
in the rest of the world? (Tigers, elephants, whales, manatee . . .)

☞ You can see my "Sasquatch" friend in the video, "10 Crunchy Carrots".

ACTIVITIES

☞ Create your own "Baby Sasquatch" Puppet using a big woolen sock with buttons for eyes and red wool for a
mouth. Attach arms and legs made from smaller socks that are stuffed with rags or tissue paper.
Sew the arms into a circle so that your "Baby Sasquatch" can give you a hug.

☞ Draw Sasquatch in the forest with his other wild animal friends or his Sasquatch family.

☞ Sing the song, taking turns being the Leader and the Echo. Have you ever heard an echo when you call
someone in the mountains? The echo is always softer.

☞ Sometimes we feel shy and need to know that we are
welcome in a group. Use this song to call someone to
circle time. Or have someone hide (like Sasquatch),
then everyone sings the song with that child's name
until he appears in the circle.

Other Echo Songs
"Little Sir Echo", "Zulu Carol", "I am a Pizza",
"Puddles" , "The Days of the Week".
Songs about the forest -
"What Kind of Tree Are You?",
"The Forest Is Calling".

SASQUATCH
(Big Foot)

By: Charlotte Diamond

♩ = 152

C / **F** / **G**

1. Sas - quatch, *Sas - quatch,* won't you come on down?
2. Sas - quatch, *Sas - quatch,* we are just like you.

C / **F** / **G**

Sas - quatch, *Sas - quatch,* won't you come on down?
Sas - quatch, *Sas - quatch,* we get fright - ened too.

F / **G** / **C** / **Am**

Shed your furry coat, and let the sun shine in,
May - be you could learn to trust us as a friend,

to CODA last time

F / **G7** / 𝄋 **C** / 1. / 2. *BRIDGE*

the door is open come on in. When you're

Am *mysteriously* / **C**

hi - ding in the moun - tains so lone - ly and a - fraid,

Credits: By Charlotte Diamond, as recorded on "10 Carrot Diamond"
© Charlotte Diamond Music Inc. 1985 SOCAN

SPIDER'S WEB

By: Charlotte Diamond

Take the sil - ver thread of a spi - der's web and spin, spin,
spin, sil - ver wings to fly and sing u -

Credits: By Charlotte Diamond, as recorded on "10 Carrot Diamond"
© Charlotte Diamond Music Inc. 1985 SOCAN

Take the silver **thread**, (pulling a thread)

of a **spider's** web,

and **spin**, **spin**, **spin**. (hands spin around each other)

Silver **wings**,

to fly and **sing**, (music)

upon the **wind**,

High above the **trees**, (forest)

across the **seas**,

and through the **sky**,

To the **rainbow's** bend,

where **stories never end**,

and dreams **never**

die.

LA TOILE D'ARAIGNÉE

French version of "Spider's Web"
By Charlotte Diamond 1985 SOCAN
As recorded on "Qu'il y ait toujours le soleil"

Prends la toile d'une araignée
Et file, file, file
Des ailes d'argent
Qui volent et chantent
Sur le vent.

Au-dessus de la forêt, au-dessus de la mer
Sur un arc-en-ciel
Où tes histoires et tous tes rêves
Ne meurent jamais.

LA TELA DE ARAÑA

Spanish version of "Spider's Web"
By Charlotte Diamond 1994 SOCAN
As recorded on "Soy una Pizza"

Toma la tela de araña
E hila, hila, hila
Las alas de plata que vuelan y cantan
Sobre el viento.

Sobre la selva, a través del mar
En el cielo azul
Hasta el arco iris de las ilusiones
Y sueños sin fin.

IDEAS & ACTIVITIES for SPIDER'S WEB

DISCUSSION IDEAS

- How many legs does a spider have? How is a spider different from an insect? How does a spider spin a web? How does a web trap insects? Are there other ways that spiders catch their prey (Trapdoor, Wolf and Tarantula spiders)? What is the largest spider in the world? Why are people sometimes afraid of spiders?

- The beauty of nature can inspire stories and songs. This song was written while I watched a tiny spider spin its web in my backyard. Take time to watch the tiny creatures of our world, like "Slimy the Slug" and "The Wee Kirkcudbright Centipede", who lives in Scotland.

ACTIVITIES

- Learn the sign language for this song. Can you sing this song in French, "La toile d'araignée" or Spanish, "La tela de araña"? The sign language is the same, in any language.

- Using a ribbon stick, move to the music and spin a web in the air.

- Draw a picture while listening to the music. Travel into the world of imagination. Let your pencil be your guide. Try drawing with your eyes closed.

- Try drawing on a big piece of paper with both hands at the same time.

- Use a parachute to represent the web. One child sits in the centre while the other children on the edge move the parachute up and down. A soft nerf ball is thrown onto the web to represent the "fly". The spider waits until the ball bounces or rolls close enough to catch. *There are wonderful suggestions for play with parachutes in "Play Power" by Sharron Werlin Krull and Norma Don (see Bibliography)*

LISA.

> **Other Songs about Interesting Creatures**
> "The Wee Kirkcudbright Centipede",
> "Fly High Unicorn", "Slimy the Slug",
> "Dragons and Dinosaurs".

OCTOPUS
(Slippery Fish)

By: Charlotte Diamond

1. Slip - pery fish, Slip - pery fish, sli - ding through the wa - ter. Slip - pery fish, Slip - pery fish,
2. Oc - to - pus, Oc - to - pus, squig - gling in the wa - ter. Oc - to - pus, Oc - to - pus,
3. Tu - na fish, Tu - na fish, flash - ing in the wa - ter. Tu - na fish, Tu - na fish,

GULP ! GULP ! GULP !

OH, NO! It's been eat - en by.. a.. OH, NO ! It's been eat -en by.. a..

Great White shark   Great White shark,   lurk-ing in the wa-ter

Great White shark,   Great White shark,   GULP! GULP! GULP!

OH! NO!   It's been eat-en by.. a.. Hu-mon-gous whale, Hu-mon-gous whale,

spout - ing in the wa - ter. Hu -mon -gous whale, Hu - mon -gous whale,

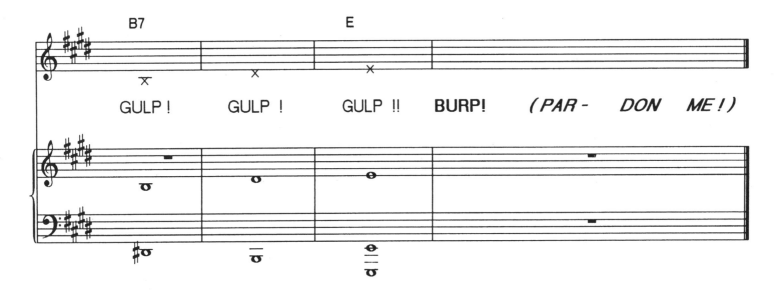

GULP ! GULP ! GULP !! BURP! (PAR - DON ME !)

Credits: By Charlotte Diamond, as recorded on "10 Carrot Diamond"
© Charlotte Diamond Music 1985 SOCAN

UN PULPITO

Spanish version of "Octopus" by C. Diamond, recorded on "Soy una Pizza"
© Charlotte Diamond Music 1985 SOCAN

Una sardina, una sardina, nadando en el agua
Una sardina, una sardina...glú, glú, glú,
Oh, no, fue comida por...

Un pulpito, un pulpito, nadando en el agua
Un pulpito, un pulpito...glú, glú, glú...
Oh, no, fue comido por...

Un atún, un atún, nadando en el agua
Un atún, un atún...glú, glú, glú...
Oh, no, fue comido por...

Un tiburón, un tiburón, nadando en el agua
Un tiburón, un tiburón...glú, glú, glú...
Oh, no, fue comido por...

Una ballena, una ballena, nadando en el agua
Una ballena, una ballena...¡GLU, GLU, GLU!
¡Perdóname!

LA BELLE PIEUVRE

French Version of "Octopus" by C. Diamond, recorded on "Qu'il y ait toujours le soleil"
© Charlotte Diamond Music 1985 SOCAN

Un petit poisson, petit poisson
Nage, nage, nage
Petit poisson, petit poisson, glou, glou, glou
Oh! Non, il est mangé par une...

Belle pieuvre, belle pieuvre
Nage, nage, nage
Belle pieuvre, belle pieuvre, glou, glou, glou
Oh! Non, elle est mangée par un...

Barracuda, barracuda
Nage, nage, nage
Barracuda, barracuda, glou, glou, glou
Oh! Non, il est mangé par un...

Grand requin, grand requin
Nage, nage, nage
Grand requin, grand requin, glou, glou, glou
Oh! Non, il est mangé par une...

Grosse baleine, grosse baleine
Nage, nage, nage
Grosse baleine, grosse baleine
Glou! Glou! Glou!... Excusez-moi!

IDEAS & ACTIVITIES for OCTOPUS

DISCUSSION IDEAS

🐙 Which animal has eight legs but it is not a spider? We know that some animals eat plants - **herbivores**; some animals eat other animals - **carnivores**; and some animals eat both - **omnivores**. There is a food chain from the smallest plankton in the sea to the biggest whale or shark. Is a whale a fish? What other mammals live in the ocean?

ACTIVITIES

🐙 Put on your imaginary wet suit, flippers, mask and snorkel (or air tanks) and dive to the bottom of the sea. Act out the different animals in this song, using sign language or your own actions. Change the words, adding other creatures that live in the ocean.

🐙 Sing the song with animals that live in fresh water - water beetles, crayfish, trout, pike.

🐙 Sing the song with dinosaurs.
    "Stegosaurus, Stegosaurus, stomping in the marshes,
     Stegosaurus, Stegosaurus, Gulp, Gulp, Gulp!
     Oh, No! It's been eaten by a . . . Tyrannosaurus!"

🐙 Sing the "Octopus" song in French - "La belle pieuvre" or in Spanish - "Un pulpito".

🐙 Make stick puppets by attaching paper cutouts of each of the animals to a craft stick. Show the proper size relationship. Or use a felt board with different-sized felt animals, one placed over the other as the animals get larger.

🐙 Make an ocean picture - blue and green crepe paper twisted together around the edges for water, torn or cutout pieces of paper pasted on the bottom for rocks, fish painted with many colours pasted onto the background, and seaweed made from strips of green and blue crepe paper trailing downward.

🐙 Make an alphabet of ocean creatures: Anchovy, Barracuda, Crab, Dolphin, Eel

Other Fun Songs
"Listen to the Water", "Rubber Blubber Whale",
"Dicky Dinosaur".
"I'm Being Eaten by a Boa Constrictor"

PUDDLES

By: Charlotte Diamond

Credits: By Charlotte Diamond, as recorded on "My Bear Gruff"   © Charlotte Diamond Music 1992 SOCAN

PUDDLES

By Charlotte Diamond, as recorded on "My Bear Gruff"
© Charlotte Diamond Music 1992 SOCAN

Intro
I'm ready for; you're ready for;
we're ready for the puddles.

1.
I've got new boots... a raincoat, too...
I've got a hat... and it's bright blue...
The sky is gray... raining cats and dogs...
And I'm ready for, you're ready for,
  we're ready for the puddles.

2.
I don't care... if it rains all day...
I can't wait... to go out and play...
Splishing and splashing... my cares away...
'Cause I'm ready for; you're ready for;
  we're ready for the puddles.

BRIDGE
The biggest ones are like a lake
What a splash we can make!
We won't get wet with all this gear
We'll stay in this puddle for a year
  (or two or three or four!)

3.
I'll catch the drips... on my tongue...
Drinking the rain... is lots of fun...
I feel like a frog... as I hop and run...
'Cause I'm ready for; you're ready for;
  we're ready for the puddles.

4.
I hear the rain... on my hat...
Tapping out... a pitter, patter, pat...
While my boots... go Smack, Smack, Smack!...
'Cause I'm ready for; you're ready for;
  we're ready for the puddles.

BRIDGE (2)
But, Hey, what's that up in the sky?
The sun peaks through and winks his eye
With the rain he's having fun
Painting a rainbow for everyone.

Repeat verse 1

CODA:
 'Cause I'm ready for; you're ready for;
we're ready for... Puddles! SPLASH!

THE MOUNTAINS

A winter version of "Puddles", By Charlotte Diamond 1992 SOCAN
© Charlotte Diamond Music Inc.

I'm ready for; you're ready for;
we're ready for the Mountains!

1.
I've got new boots...and new skis, too...
  (a snowboard, too)
I've got a touque (hat)...and it's bright blue...
The sky is gray...and it looks like snow...
I'm ready for; you're ready for;
  we're ready for the Mountains!

2.
I don't care...if it snows all day...
I can't wait...to go out and play...
Slipping and sliding...my cares away...
I'm ready for; you're ready for;
  we're ready for the Mountains!

BRIDGE
The biggest hills are lots of fun
I want to ski down every one
I won't get tired, I'll ski all day
As long as my family will pay...for years and
  years and years!

3.
I catch the flakes...on my tongue...
Munching the snow...is lots of fun...
I hop like a frog...down every run...
I'm ready for; you're ready for;
  we're ready for the Mountains!

4.
I love the jumps...and moguls, too
The peanut trails...are fun to do...
Just take your pick...green, black or blue...
I'm ready for; you're ready for;
  we're ready for the Mountains!

BRIDGE (2)
But, hey, what's that up in the sky?
The sun peeks through and winks his eye
With the snow he's having fun
Making it sparkle for everyone.

Repeat verse one
CODA: "Cause I'm ready for; you're ready for;
  we're ready for the Mountains! SWISH!

IDEAS & ACTIVITIES for PUDDLES

DISCUSSION IDEAS

➤ Why do we need the rain? How is rain formed? When it turns colder, what falls instead of rain?
Do you like to jump into puddles? Be careful not to splash your friends unless they want to play the puddle game, too. How do puddles disappear?

ACTIVITIES

➤ Make an imaginary puddle on the floor (use a hula hoop or rope) and pretend that you are jumping into the puddle, splashing everyone with imaginary water. How would you act if you were soaked and dripping?
You can use the same puddle when you dive underwater, looking for Octopus.

➤ Dance with an umbrella that is passed from one person to another. Umbrellas are fun to twirl or hide behind.
A parachute can be an umbrella. Some children hold the parachute up while others take turns being under the "umbrella".

➤ Take turns being the Leader and the Echo. Make up actions to go with the words. Clap your hands when you say the word "puddles".

➤ **The Rain Storm** - Divide your group into three sections. When the leader points to a section, everyone in that group makes the sound of rain by tapping the fingers of one hand against the palm of the other. The leader raises her hand to make the sound louder or lowers her hand to make it softer (like the conductor of an orchestra). The groups are added on until everyone is "making rain". Then one by one, each group becomes quieter until the rain storm stops. A fourth group could be the wind. Children love having the chance to be the "conductor".
A rain stick can be added to begin and end the storm.

➤ **The Puddle Game** - Using several sets of boots and rain gear (all washable!), make puddles outside on a flat surface and invite several children to "splash" along to the music. Add washable, water-diluted tempera paints to make more colourful puddles. Make footprints with your boots. When you mix two different colours, you can make new colours. (Red and blue make the colour purple. Blue and yellow make the colour green.)
Be sure to have several large water-filled spray bottles for clean up. Spray the surface clean before inviting the next group to play in the puddles.
This suggestion came from Mackie Rhodes, in "The Mailbox" Teacher's Magazine.
June/July 1998 Kindergarten Edition

➤ Write a new version of this song with "Snow"
"I'm ready for, you're ready for, we're ready for the snowfall!
I've got new boots . . . new mittens, too . . .
I've got a toque (hat) . . . and it's bright blue . . .
The sky is gray . . . and it looks like snow . . .
I'm ready for, you're ready for, we're ready for the snowfall!"

➤ *Here is a version sent to me by Charlotte Carnevale in Los Altos, CA*
"Oh, Spring has sprung . . . all things are new . . .
I planted seeds . . . And they sure grew . . .
Oh, Spring has sprung . . . It's in the air . . .
And I'm ready for, you're ready for, we're ready for springtime!

➤ Make a "Big Book" for your new version and for the original version of this song.

Other Weather Songs
"It's a Rainy Day",
"Hello Winter" (Bonjour l'hiver),
"May There Always Be Sunshine",
"Sing in the Spring".

METAMORPHOSIS

by Charlotte Diamond, as recorded on "Diamond in the Rough"
© Charlotte Diamond Music 1986 SOCAN

1.
Once I was a tadpole, squiggling all around
I watched those bigger frogs all hopping on the ground
I was proud that I could swim and catch bugs all day
I didn't know I would change in a very mysterious way

CHORUS
That's Metamorphosis, just Metamorphosis
That's how a little tadpole becomes a hopping frog
Or a butterfly grows wings on a creepy, crawling thing
That's Metamorphosis, just Metamorphosis

2.
Then one day two bumps appeared on either side of my tail
Two more bumps came later on, on either side of my head
They grew and grew into arms and legs and my tail just
  disappeared
All these changes came too fast and I felt really weird
But my Mom said, "That's okay..."

CHORUS

3.
Gosh, I found it hard to breathe underwater all day
I swam to the top and took a "GULP",
  that seemed an easier way
Then one day I was chasing a fly and
  I hopped out on the land
I looked at myself and "LO AND BEHOLD",
  I was a frog so grand! Thanks to....Metamorphosis.

CHORUS

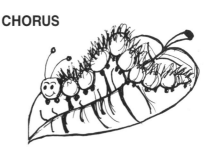

IDEAS & ACTIVITIES for METAMORPHOSIS

DISCUSSION IDEAS

✳ Do you know some examples of "Metamorphosis"? A tadpole changes into a frog or toad.
A caterpillar changes into a butterfly or a moth. Do you know the different stages of metamorphosis for a
butterfly? Caterpillar (larva), pupa (in the cocoon) and butterfly (adult).

✳ We all grow and change throughout our lives. Sometimes those changes are not easy. Sometimes we are not
sure that we will become something attractive. Will everyone still like us? What are some changes that are
difficult? For example, moving, changing schools, making new friends, growing taller...etc.

✳ Can you do something now that you could not do one year ago?
What would you like to do when you are older?

✳ Do you know the story of the "Frog Prince"?

ACTIVITIES

✳ Act out the words while singing the song. Imagine that you are changing from a
tadpole to a frog. What can you do as a frog that you could not do as a tadpole?

✳ Imagine that you are a creeping caterpillar. You eat and eat and eat! Then you sleep in your cocoon.
Finally, you awake and stretch your wings. "Fly away beautiful butterfly!"

✳ **Frog Game** - Form a circle. One person is chosen to be the frog who hops inside the circle. A nerf ball is the fly
that is passed from one person to another by bouncing into or throwing across the circle. The frog catches the
fly and the last person to throw the fly (ball) becomes the new frog.

✳ Draw a picture of the creatures that go through metamorphosis.

✳ There are many lovely puppets available that change
from a tadpole to a frog or a caterpillar to a butterfly.

✳ Songs and stories about growing up -
"Roots and Wings", "My Favourite Things",
"Find Your Spot",
"You Never Praise Me Enough", and the book
"Little Gorilla", by Ruth Bornstein.

Other Froggy & Butterfly Songs
"The Foolish Frog", "Five Green and Speckled
Frogs" (Raffi) and the book,
"A Very Hungry Caterpillar", by Eric Carle

METAMORPHOSIS

By: Charlotte Diamond

♩ = 186

1. Once I was a tad - pole squig - ling all a - round; I watched those big - ger frogs all hop - ping on the ground. I was proud that I could swim and catch bugs all day, I did - n't know that I would change in a ve - ry mys - te - ri - ous way--- That's Me - ta morph - pho - sis,

Credits: by Charlotte Diamond, as recorded on "Diamond in the Rough"
            ©Charlotte Diamond Music 1986 SOCAN

DAYS OF THE WEEK

By: Charlotte Diamond

Credits: By Charlotte Diamond, as recorded on "Diamond in the Rough" (solo by Thomas Diamond)
© Charlotte Diamond Music 1986 SOCAN

THE DAYS OF THE WEEK

By Charlotte Diamond, as recorded on "Diamond in the Rough"
© Charlotte Diamond Music 1986 SOCAN

1. English:
Monday, Tuesday, Wednesday, Thursday
Friday, Saturday, Sunday
Let's sing the days of the week.

2. French:
Lundi, mardi, mercredi, jeudi,
Vendredi, samedi, dimanche
Chantons les jours de la semaine.

3. Spanish:
Lunes, martes, miercoles, jueves,
Viernes, sabado, domingo
Los días de la semana.

Repeat verse 1.

SIGN LANGUAGE

Monday   Tuesday   Wednesday   Thursday

Friday   Saturday   Sunday

Jessica

IDEAS & ACTIVITIES for DAYS OF THE WEEK

DISCUSSION IDEAS

🚲 Do you know the days of the week, the months of the year and the seasons?
Can you say the "Days of the Week" in different languages? It is easier to
learn a language when you echo the words.

ACTIVITIES

🚲 Learn to sing the days of the week in French and Spanish. Then learn the days of the week in other languages.

🚲 Learn the days of the week in sign language.

🚲 How many different languages are spoken by children in your class?
In your school? In your community? Find on a world map where
these languages are spoken.

🚲 Sing this song in different languages for a Family Day at your school.

🚲 Take turns being the Leader and the Echo.
This song is a good choice for learning to sing solo.

Other Echo Songs
"I Am a Pizza", "Puddles",
"Sasquatch", "Zulu Carol".
Songs about the seasons -
"Hello Winter", "Bonjour l'hiver",
"Sing In the Spring".

MAY THERE ALWAYS BE SUNSHINE

Music by: A. Ostrovsky
Russian words by: A. Oshanin

English words by: Tom Botting
Adapted by: Charlotte Diamond

May there al - ways be sun - shine, may there al - ways be blue skies, may there al - ways be Ma - ma, may there al - ways be me.

Russian
Poost vzeg -

(Recorded in the key of E)

Russian (sound writing)
Poost vzegda boodyit solnse
Poost vzegda boodyit nieba
Poost vzegda boodyit mama
Poost vzegda boodoo ya

Spanish
Que haya siempre sol
Que haya siempre cielo
Que esté siempre mi mami
Que esté siempre yo

Cantonese (sound writing)
Tun hay mong seung yau tie yeung
Tun hay mong seung yau ching teen
Tun hay mong seung yau mama
Tun hay mong seung yau nga

French
Qu'il y ait toujours le soleil
Qu'il y ait toujours le ciel bleu
Qu'il y ait toujours ma maman
Et que je sois toujours là

German
Immer scheine die sonne
Immer strahle der himmel
Immer lebe die mutti
Un auch ich immerdar

Italian
Que ci sia sempre el sole
Que ci sia cielo azurro
Que ci sia sempre mamma
Que ci sia sempre me

Hebrew (sound writing)
Loo ye hee ta meed shemesh
Loo ye hee ta meed shamaim
Loo ye hee ta meed eema
Loo ye hee ta meed anee

Norwegian (sound writing)
La day alteed blee solshin
May en himmel so blo
La day alteed ha mama
La day alteed blee may

Sarah.

SIGN LANGUAGE

May there
always be

sunshine
(form a circle overhead)

blue sky

Mama

Papa

me

brother

sister

family

friends

IDEAS & ACTIVITIES for MAY THERE ALWAYS BE SUNSHINE

DISCUSSION IDEAS

✺ A young Russian boy drew a picture of the sun in a blue sky, a picture of his mama and himself.
Then he wrote the poem:
> May there always be sunshine,
> May there always be blue skies
> May there always be Mama,
> May there always be me.

A Russian composer added music to the poem, and now this folk song is known all over the world, in many languages.

✺ What does the song mean to you? Think of other things that we wish there would always be, such as, our family and friends, lions, tigers, elephants, whales, pandas, grizzly bears, forests, oceans, pure water...pizza! The possibilities are endless.

ACTIVITIES

✺ Learn the song in sign language. Add in the signs for father, brother, sister, family and friends. Learn the signs for the endangered animals that you wish there would always be.

✺ Try singing the song in other languages. You may need some help from families in your community who speak that language. Do you speak another language? Can you translate this song into your language and teach your friends?

✺ This is an excellent "Zipper" song. Add these words: "May there always be sunlight, moonlight, starlight and me." Or name the planets: Mercury, Venus, Mars and Earth.

✺ Make a mobile of this song with a coat hanger covered with blue paper. Suspend and balance from strings the sun and pictures of your family and yourself.

✺ Draw a picture of children around the world, singing this song of peace.

✺ Make a big sun to go over and around the entrance to your room or classroom. Then every day is a sunny day!

Other Peace Songs
"Earth, Water, Air and Fire", "Everyday Angel", "Tout ce que je veux - la paix" (All I really want is Peace) and "I'd Like to Teach the World to Sing".

EVERYDAY ANGEL

By: Charlotte Diamond

EVERYDAY ANGEL

By Charlotte Diamond, as recorded on "Diamonds and Daydreams"
© 1994 Charlotte Diamond Music SOCAN

CHORUS
Be an Everyday Angel
Help out in little ways
Share your smile
And make this a better day
Be an Everyday Angel
Spread your wings
Bringing your love to all that
  you touch
Makes their hearts sing.

1.
Each day has its problems
Sometimes it's hard to take
The world moves too fast
From the moment that we awake
But then there are Angels
To see us through
And the very best Angels with
  tiny wings
Are me and you.

2.
It isn't the biggest gift
That brings the biggest smile
But gentle memories
That stay with us awhile
Of times together
Feeling close
Sharing our dreams, sharing
  our fears,
Sharing our hopes.

CHORUS

SIGN LANGUAGE

Be an **Everyday**   **Angel**.   **Help** out   in **little**

ways.   **Share**   your **smile**   and **make** this

a **better**   **day**.   Be an **Everyday**   **Angel**.

Spread your wings,   **bringing**   your **love**   to **all** that

you   **touch,**   makes their **hearts**   **sing**.

IDEAS AND ACTIVITIES for EVERYDAY ANGEL

DISCUSSION IDEAS

- Do you have a favourite auntie, uncle, grandma or grandpa or special friend? Someone who thinks you are just great? Someone who loves you and watches over you? Someone who is your champion when times are tough? That person is your **Everyday Angel**.

- As we grow, we learn to be an "Everyday Angel" for others. The little things in life are often the most important, such as a smile, a helping hand or someone who will listen to our problems. When we help others, we feel better about ourselves. What did you do today to make this world just a little bit better?

- **"Leave the world just a little bit better than the way it was in the morning."**

ACTIVITIES

- Learn the sign language for the chorus. How does it feel to spread your wings and fly?

- Clean up your classroom or backyard. Make Everyday Angels and Hug Bugs and take them to a local home or meeting place for Seniors. These grandmas and grandpas would love to hear you sing these songs as well as "Four Hugs a Day". Share your music as well as your smile.

- Be an Everyday Angel at home, too. Help out by making your bed or tidying your games without having to be asked. Hum or whistle a song while you work.

- Draw a picture of your Everyday Angel, then hang the angel over your bed.

> ## Other Songs with Wings
> "Roots and Wings", "Five Little Sparrows", "Fly High Unicorn", "Wounded Bird", "Spider's Web", "The Giving Tree".

~Nikki~

EACH OF US IS A FLOWER

By: Charlotte Diamond

Credits: By Charlotte Diamond, as recorded on "10 Carrot Diamond" © Charlotte Diamond Music SOCAN 1984

(This song is recorded in the key of E)

CHORUS (X2)
Each of us is a flower
Growing in life's garden
Each of us is a flower
We need the sun and rain.

VERSE
Sun, shine your warmth on me
Moon, cool me with your night
Wind, bring the gentle rain
Earth, take my roots down deep.

SOMOS COMO LAS FLORES

Spanish version of "Each of us is a Flower"
By Charlotte Diamond 1994 SOCAN
As recorded on "Soy una Pizza"

CORO

Somos como las flores
En el jardín de la vida
Somos como las flores
Necesitamos la lluvia y el sol

VERSO

Sol, caliéntame
Luna, arrúllame
Brisa, refréscame
Tierra, aliméntame.

NOUS SOMMES TOUS COMME LES FLEURS

French version of "Each of us is a Flower"
By Charlotte Diamond 1984 SOCAN

REFRAIN

Nous sommes tous comme les fleurs
Dans le jardin de la vie
Nous sommes tous comme les fleurs
Il nous faut le soleil et la pluie.

COUPLET

Soleil, réchauffe-moi
Lune, berce-moi
Brise, rafraîchis-moi
Terre, nourris-moi.

IDEAS AND ACTIVITIES for EACH OF US IS A FLOWER

DISCUSSION IDEAS

❀ What do seeds need to help them grow? (Sunshine, water, earth, compost) When do we plant seeds?

❀ What kind of flower would you like to be? What do we need to help us grow? (Friends, family, hugs, books, pets, food, sunshine... etc.) Many children in our world do not have clean water, enough food, a home or teachers to help them grow and learn. Through organizations such as UNICEF, we can help children who are less fortunate than we are. ***"I am a Special Representative for UNICEF Canada, and I have travelled to Costa Rica to visit some UNICEF school projects. UNICEF helps many children around the world receive a better education and live a healthier, happier life."***

ACTIVITIES

❀ Act out the words to "Each of us is a Flower". Imagine that you are a seed in the ground. As you are touched by the Sun, Moon, Wind and Rain, you begin to slowly grow and bloom into a beautiful flower. Make a sun, moon and rain cloud out of paper, and attach each to a stick. The wind can be a ribbon stick. These props may also be useful for "May There Always Be Sunshine", "The Garden Song" and the story, "The Wisest Old Woman and Man".

❀ Divide into two groups. One group sings the **Chorus** while the second group sings the **Verse**. The two parts harmonize.

DAVE

❀ Change the words and make up a new song.
"Each of us is a flower growing in life's garden.
Each of us is a flower, we need our families and friends"

❀ Draw your favourite flower with your face or your photo in the centre.

❀ Make a large flower with a hole in the centre for your face. (Suggestion from Patti Haire, Las Vegas) See also **Activities** for "I am a Pizza".

❀ Start some seeds indoors or in a green house, and transplant outdoors when the weather is warmer. Can you tell the difference between a carrot seed and a bean seed?

❀ Start a bean seed growing in a clear plastic cup filled with a paper towel, soaked with water. "First the roots grow down and then the plant grows up."
Then plant your bean sprout into soil.

❀ Study some different kinds of soils, noticing the smell, texture and colour. Which soil has mostly sand, clay or decayed plants? Which soil holds the most water? When you add compost or mulch (decayed plants), the soil becomes richer and holds more water

❀ Visit a public garden or look for wildflowers in the woods. Keep a list of flowers that you have seen - roses, pansies, snapdragons, dandelions, tiger lilies, skunk cabbage. Some wildflowers have wild animal names.

Other Growing Songs
"The Garden Song", "Wildflowers",
"10 Crunchy Carrots". "The Giving Tree",
"What Kind of Tree Are You?"

Each of us is a **flower**

growing

in life's **garden**.

Each of us is a **flower**

We need the **sun**

and **rain**

Sun,

shine your warmth on **me.**

Moon

cool me with your night.

Wind,

bring the gentle **rain.**

Earth,

take my **roots** **down** **deep.**

I AM A PIZZA

By: PETER ALSOP

Credits: By Peter Alsop (Moose School Music BMI) French translation by Charlotte Diamond
Charlotte Diamond Music, 1988 SOCAN

I AM A PIZZA (JE SUIS UNE PIZZA)

By Peter Alsop (Moose School Music BMI)
French translation by Charlotte Diamond
Charlotte Diamond Music, 1988 SOCAN

SOY UNA PIZZA

Spanish translation by Charlotte Diamond
Charlotte Diamond Music 1993 (SOCAN)
From the English "I am a Pizza"
by Peter Alsop

ENGLISH
(on "10 Carrot Diamond")

1.
I am a pizza
With extra cheese
From tomatoes
Sauce is squeezed
Onions and mushrooms
Oregano!!
I am a pizza
Ready to go!

2.
I am a pizza
Pepperoni
No anchovies
Or "Phony Bologna"
I am a pizza
Order by phone
I am a pizza
Please take me home.

3.
I am a pizza
Peppers on top
Out on the oven
Into the box
Into the car and
Upside-down!
I am a pizza
Dropped on the ground.

4.
I was a pizza
I was the best
I was a pizza
Now I'm a mess!

FRENCH
(on "Qu'il y ait toujours le soleil")

1.
Je suis une pizza
Avec du fromage
Beaucoup de sauce
Des tomates
Des oignons, des champignons
Épices mélangées
Je suis une pizza
Prête à manger

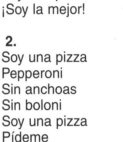

2.
Je suis un pizza
Pepperoni
Pas d'anchois
Ou "Phony Bologna"
Je suis une pizza
Téléphone-moi
Je suis une pizza
Apporte-moi chez toi.

3.
Je suis une pizza
Du poivron vert
Je vais du four
Jusqu'à la boite
Dans la voiture
À l'envers
Je suis une pizza
Tombée par terre

4.
J'étais une pizza
Trésor de la cuisine
J'étais une pizza
Tombée en ruine!

SPANISH
(on "Soy una Pizza")

1.
Soy una pizza
Con mucho queso
Llena de salsa
De tomate
Cebollas y hongos
Orégano
Soy una pizza
¡Soy la mejor!

2.
Soy una pizza
Pepperoni
Sin anchoas
Sin boloni
Soy una pizza
Pídeme
Soy una pizza
Ya llévame

3.
Soy una pizza
Pimiento verde
Salí del horno
Hacia la caja
Pero en el coche
¡Me caí!
Soy una pizza
¡Pobre de mí!

4.
Fuí una pizza
Fuí la mejor
Una linda pizza
¡Ahora ya no!

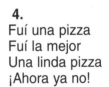

IDEAS AND ACTIVITIES for I AM A PIZZA

DISCUSSION IDEAS

⊕ What is your favourite kind of pizza? How do we make a pizza? What are the ingredients?
Some of the toppings, such as tomatoes, peppers and onions can be grown in your garden.
A good companion song is the "Garden Song".

⊕ Did you know that pizza originally came from Italy? Name some foods that come from other lands, such as
Polish sausage, Chinese Won Ton soup, Japanese sushi, Mexican tacos.

ACTIVITIES

⊕ This is an excellent echo song and very easy to sing. Divide into two groups, one group leads while the second
group echoes. One child may want to be the leader.

⊕ When you know the song in English, try singing in French, **"Je suis une pizza"** or Spanish, **"Soy una pizza"**.

⊕ Use a felt board with the pizza shape and add different felt toppings.

⊕ Act out the words with a pizza box and a felt pizza inside.

⊕ Draw your favourite pizza. Be creative with your toppings! Do you like pineapple?

⊕ As you did with "Each of Us is A Flower", make a large paper pizza with a hole in the centre for your face.
Laminate the pizza to make it last longer.

⊕ Change the words of the song to suit the toppings. " I am a Pizza... with lots of olives, some feta cheese,
red peppers, too . . . "

⊕ Make pizzas in class so that you really **are** a pizza. (You are what you eat!)

⊕ Change the word "Pizza" to other foods, such as, "sandwich" and "taco". Create a new song by adding the word
"guitar" (the Zipper Method).
"I'm a guitar . . . made of wood . . . , When you strum me . . . I sound good . . . "
"I'm a guitar . . . zing, zing, zing . . . , I'm a guitar, I help you sing!"

Other Echo Songs & Stories
"Sasquatch", "Looking for Dracula",
"Puddles" and "The Zulu Carol",
"The Days of the Week".

LA BAMBA

Traditional
Arranged and Translated by: Charlotte Diamond

VERSE 1

Pa - ra bai - lar La Bam - ba, pa - ra bai - lar La Bam -

ba, se ne - ce - si - ta un po - qui - to de gra - cia, un po - qui - to de gra -

cia y ot - ra co - si - ta Ay! ar - ri - ba, ar - ri - ba, Ay! ar - ri - ba, ar -

ri - ba, ar - ri - ba, i - re por ti se - re, por ti se - re. CHORUS Bam - ba, Bam -

ba, Bam - ba, la Bam - ba, la Bam - ba, Bam - ba, Bam - ba,

1,2,3 Bam - ba, la Bam - ba, la Bam. 4 Bam - ba, la Bam - ba, la Bam - ba, Bam - ba, Bam -

ba, Bam - ba, la Bam - ba, la Bam - ba, La Bam - ba!

Credits: Folk song from Veracruz, México
Musical arrangement, English and French translations by Charlotte Diamond
1985 SOCAN   As recorded on "Soy una Pizza", "10 Carrot Diamond" & "Qu'il y ait toujours le soleil".

LA BAMBA

Folk song from Veracruz, México
Musical arrangement, English and French translations by Charlotte Diamond
1985 SOCAN   As recorded on "Soy una Pizza"

1.
Para bailar la Bamba
Para bailar la Bamba
Se necesita una poca de gracia
Una poca de gracia y otra cosita
Ay! arriba y arriba, Ay! arriba y arriba y arriba iré
Por ti seré, por ti seré

CORO
Bamba, Bamba; Bamba, La Bamba, La Bamba
Bamba, Bamba; Bamba, La Bamba, La Bamba

2.
Para subir al cielo
Para subir al cielo
Se necesita una escalera grande
Una escalera grande y otra chiquita
Ay! arriba y arriba, Ay! arriba y arriba y arriba iré
Por ti seré, por ti seré   **CORO**

3.
Una niña en un baile
Una niña en un baile
Se lamentaba zapatito de raso
Zapatito de raso, que le apretaba
Ay! Arriba y arriba.... etc.
Por ti seré, por ti seré   **CORO**

4.
Repeat verse 1 and Chorus

**English version of Verse 1 on
"10 Carrot Diamond"**

When you dance La Bamba
When you dance La Bamba
All you need is a little bit of rhythm
A little bit of rhythm, clap your hands

**French version of Verse 1 on
"Qu'il y ait toujours le soleil"**

Quand tu danses La Bamba, quand tu danses
 La Bamba
Tout ce qu'il faut, c'est un peu de rythme
Un peu de rythme, un peu d'élégance.

English translation of Verses 2 and 3
2.
To get to heaven, to get to heaven
What you will need is a very long ladder
A very long ladder and a short one, too.

3.
Once a girl at a dance (a ball), once a girl at
 a dance
Sadly lamented that her shoes of satin
That her shoes of satin were too tight.

IDEAS AND ACTIVITIES for LA BAMBA

DISCUSSION IDEAS

 This favourite dance tune in Spanish comes from Vera Cruz, Mexico and is well known all over the world. "Hables español?" Do you know some words in Spanish, such as, Buenos Días (Good Day), Adiós (Goodbye), or foods like tacos, burritos, salsa and tortilla chips?

ACTIVITIES

 Make your own rhythm instruments. For example, fill a yogurt container or film canister with popcorn kernels, macaroni, or rice to make shakers or maracas. A small group can play at one time so that others can listen. The sound will change when you put less or more kernels in the container. Play loudly, then softly. Play different patterns. One person can lead while the group echoes. Can you hear the difference between the sound of rice or popcorn?

 Create your own dance or a clapping pattern. Work in pairs, then share your ideas.

 To add colour and movement, dance with a flowing scarf or a ribbon stick - a long ribbon, attached to a round wooden stick. Make a figure 8, circle "S", and dragon's tail.

 To learn the words in Spanish, sing only small sections at a time, using the "Echo method".

 There are many beautiful songs in Spanish, such as, "Feliz Navidad" or "De Colores" from the recording "Soy una Pizza". Play rhythm instruments with these songs and others, like "Each of Us Is a Flower", "Love Me for Who I Am", "All the Nations Like Banana", and "Lucky Streak".

TOUT CE QUE JE VEUX - LA PAIX
(All I Really Want Is Peace)

♩ = 120   "Rock" Ballade

Par: Charlotte Diamond

TOUT CE QUE JE VEUX - LA PAIX

By Charlotte Diamond, as recorded on
"Qu'il y ait toujours le soleil"
© Charlotte Diamond Music 1984 SOCAN

Refrain
Tout ce que je veux, la paix dans le monde
Dans mon coeur et dans ma famille   (bis)

1.
Je ne veux qu'un rêve pour m'apaiser
Une chanson pour me rassurer
Et je veux savoir que nous vivrons
Toujours dans la paix.
Refrain

2.
Je voudrais vivre toute ma vie sans peur
Sans peur de demain
Je voudrais vivre toute ma vie sans peur
Et ta main dans ma main.
Refrain

TODO LO QUE QUIERO ES PAZ

Spanish Version of "Tout ce que je veux - La Paix"
As recorded on "Soy una Pizza"
© Charlotte Diamond Music 1994 SOCAN

CORO
Todo lo que quiero es paz en el mundo,
En mi corazón, y en mi familia   (bis)

1.
Quisiera tener un sueño de esperanza
Y una canción que alegre el corazón
Y quisiera saber que podemos vivir
Juntos y siempre feliz
CORO

2.
Yo quiero vivir toda mi vida, en paz
Sin miedo del mañana
Yo quiero vivir toda mi vida, en paz
Con nuestras manos unidas.
CORO

ALL I REALLY WANT IS PEACE

By Charlotte Diamond
© Charlotte Diamond Music SOCAN 1984

CHORUS
All I really want, is peace in the world
Peace in my heart and in my family.

1.
I just need a dream, to help me sleep at night
And a song to make me feel alright
I just need to know, that you and I
Can live side by side.
CHORUS

2.
I wish I could live all of my lifetime in peace
Not fearing for tomorrow
I wish I could live all of my lifetime in peace
Holding your hand in mine.
CHORUS

..Monique..

SIGN LANGUAGE

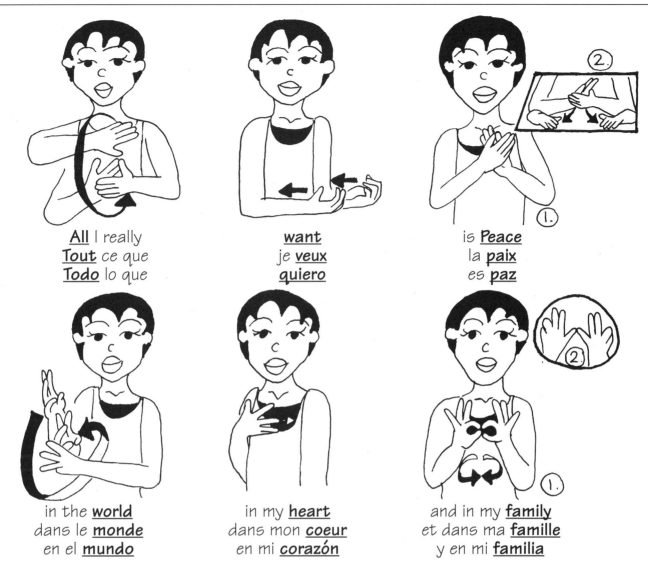

All I really
Tout ce que
Todo lo que

want
je **veux**
quiero

is **Peace**
la **paix**
es **paz**

in the **world**
dans le **monde**
en el **mundo**

in my **heart**
dans mon **coeur**
en mi **corazón**

and in my **family**
et dans ma **famille**
y en mi **familia**

IDEAS AND ACTIVITIES for TOUT CE QUE JE VEUX - LA PAIX

DISCUSSION IDEAS

⚽ This song was written first in French then translated to Spanish. There are English words provided but you may want to try to learn it first in French or Spanish.

⚽ Living peacefully starts first with ourselves (in our own heart) then moves outward to others around us. When we take good care of ourselves, we have love and good feelings to share with others. We learn about peace at home through respecting those in our family. We learn how to live together by caring, cooperating and sharing. When we go to school, we learn how to live peacefully with others who may have ideas and customs different from ours. As we learn from each other, we become citizens of the world.
"All I really want is peace in the world, peace in my heart and in my family."

⚽ What do you do when you become angry with your brother or sister or a friend? Can you see the other person's point of view? Can you think of a better way to handle your anger? Once the problem is resolved, shake hands or give a hug and continue being friends.

⚽ Sometimes we need to **Stop** and take time to **Listen**.

ACTIVITIES

⚽ Learn the sign language for the Chorus.

⚽ Imagine that you could change the world. What would you want to do? Draw a picture of your ideas.

Other Peaceful Songs
"My Bear Gruff", "Cooperation", "Why Did I Have to Have a Sister?", "Love Me for Who I Am", "May There Always Be Sunshine", "Lucky Streak", "One Dream", "Stop and Listen".

LUCKY STREAK

By: Tom Arntzen
Arranged by: Charlotte Diamond

Credits: By Tom Arntzen SOCAN 1988
            © Tom Arntzen
            As recorded on "Diamonds and Dragons" by Charlotte Diamond

LUCKY STREAK

By Tom Arntzen SOCAN 1988
© Tom Arntzen
As recorded on "Diamonds and Dragons" by Charlotte Diamond

CHORUS
I got a smile on my face, shoes on my feet
That's all I really need, I guess I got a Lucky Streak
I got the sun pouring down, the birds sing so sweet
That's all I really need, I guess I got a Lucky Streak.

1.
I don't need any money to buy those fancy toys
I'm satisfied with what I've got, I can still make lots of noise
If I had a hundred dollars to spend just how I feel
I'd give it to someone who needs it, someone not as lucky as me.
CHORUS

2.
I'm glad to have the stars, shining down so bright
I'm lucky to have the moon, to help me see at night
When I stop to think, it adds up to a lot
And makes me feel lucky, I'm happy with what I've got.
CHORUS

SIMON

QUÉ BUENA SUERTE

Spanish version of "Lucky Streak" by Tom Arntzen
Translated by Charlotte Diamond 1994 SOCAN
As recorded on "Soy una Pizza"

CORO
Tengo una cara feliz
Zapatos en mis pies
¡Qué buena suerte!
¡No necesito más!

Arriba brilla el sol
Los pajaritos cantan
¡Qué buena suerte!
¡No necesito más!

1.
No necesito dinero
Para caros jugetes
Con mi música y canciones
Mucho más yo puedo hacer
Si un millón tuviera
Para gastarlo como quisiera
Lo compartiría con alguien
Que tuviera menos que yo.
CORO

2.
Me gustan las estrellas
Que brillan en el cielo
Y la luz de la luna
Que acompaña mi dormir
Si pienso en lo que tengo
Aumenta mi riqueza
¡Qué feliz me siento!
¡No necesito más!
CORO

ACTIONS

I've got a **smile** on my face,

shoes on my feet,

That's all I really need.

I guess I got a lucky streak.

I've got the **sun** pouring down,

The **birds** sing so sweet.
The **birds** sing so sweet.

That's all I really need.

I guess I got a lucky streak.

IDEAS AND ACTIVITIES for LUCKY STREAK

DISCUSSION IDEAS

✳ In what ways are you lucky? Do all the children of the world have the same good fortune as you? Whenever you are having a **"horrible, no good, rotten day"**, think of your own "Lucky Streak". Remember, things could be worse!

✳ This song is fun to sing on a dull or rainy day.

✳ Do you know how to say "Good luck" in different languages? French - "Bonne Chance", Spanish - "Buena Suerte", Chinese?

ACTIVITIES

✳ Draw a picture of yourself, riding on your **Lucky Streak** - a rainbow or a shooting star. In your picture, draw all the things that make you feel lucky.

✳ Learn the actions to the Chorus. Create your own actions for the verses.

✳ This song is easy to sing in Spanish, **"Qué Buena Suerte"** or "What Good Luck".

Other Songs that Cheer Us Up

"My Favourite Things", "
The Whistling Paper Boy",
"The Hug Bug", "Stop and Listen",
"All the Nations Like Bananas".

ONE DREAM

By: Perry Ehrlich

Just put a dream in-side your heart and let it grow, and from the

mo-ment that you do then you will know. No mat-ter

what we all can do to make that spe-cial dream come true, from the start,

it be-gins with a dream in your heart. 1. I have but

One Dream, to build a world filled with love, peace and kind-ness, with clear

skies up a-bove. Come stand be-side me, show each

oth-er we care, let's build a dream we all can share.

2. It does-n't mat-ter what co-lour we are, be my friend I

like who you are. Sing with me then

you'll un-der-stand, let's build a dream come take my hand. I have but

SOLO

share. CHOIR It does-n't mat-ter what

I have but One Dream, to build a

co-lour we are. Be my friend I

world filled with love, peace and kind-ness, with clear

like who you are. Sing with me then

skies up a-bove. Come stand be-side me, show each

repeat to the sign

Credits: By Perry Ehrlich 1996 SOCAN
As recorded on "Diamonds and Daydreams" by Charlotte Diamond

ONE DREAM

By Perry Ehrlich 1996 SOCAN   As recorded on "Diamonds and Daydreams" by Charlotte Diamond

Intro
Just put a dream inside your heart and let it grow
And from the moment that you do then you will know
No matter what we all can do to make a special dream come true
From the start...It begins with a dream in your heart.

1.
I have but one dream to build a world filled with love
Peace and kindness with clear skies up above
Come stand beside me, show each other we care
Let's build a dream we all can share.

2.
It doesn't matter what colour we are
Be my friend, I like who you are
Sing with me, then you'll understand
Let's build a dream, come take my hand
Repeat verses 1 and 2

3.
I have one dream
We have one dream
Repeat verses 1 and 2

Tag "Just put a dream inside your heart"

SIGN LANGUAGE - Verse 1

I **have**   but **one**   **dream,**   to **build**

a **world**   filled with **love,**   **peace**   and **kindness,**

with clear **skies** **up** **above.**   **Come**   stand **beside**   **me,**

show each other,   **we**   **care.**

Let's **build**   **dream**   we **all**   can **share.**

IDEAS AND ACTIVITIES for ONE DREAM

DISCUSSION IDEAS

☆ It is important to be a dreamer, to think of ways our world can become a kinder place in which to live, a world in which everyone is respected and valued.

☆ Martin Luther King Jr. spoke the words, **"I have a dream... "** a dream that there be equality of all peoples regardless of colour or race. His speech was heard throughout the United States and around the world. His birthday, January 15, has been declared a national holiday in the USA to acknowledge his wonderful work and his vision.

☆ What are some of your dreams? Some may be little dreams and some may be big, but they are **all** important.

ACTIVITIES

> Trevor <

☆ Learn to sing the song in parts as on the recording. The SOLO part can also be sung by a group.

☆ Learn the sign language for the first Verse "I have but One Dream."

☆ Draw a picture of one of your dreams. Then combine the pictures of all of the class into one large picture. Do many of you have the same dream?

☆ Share the reasons for your dream with your classmates.

Other Songs about Dreams
"Close your Eyes", "Everyday Angel",
"Spider's Web", "Goodnight Mistress Moon",
"All Through the Night", "We Shall Overcome"

YOU CAN MAKE A MIRACLE

By: Charlotte Diamond

YOU CAN MAKE A MIRACLE

By Charlotte Diamond, as recorded on "Diamonds and Dragons"
© Charlotte Diamond Music 1988 SOCAN

CHORUS
You can make a miracle
You can help the children
Because of you, the future will be theirs

You can make a miracle
You can help the children
Reach out your hand and show them that you care.

Verse 1
There are so many children
Who need that special caring
That special time to help them on their way,
Children are the future
Each face a tomorrow
Within each smile, the sunshine of today.
CHORUS

Verse 2
The world's spinning faster
With so many needs and changes
It's hard to know what each of us can do
But just one kindness
Leads to another and another
Soon the light of love comes shining through.
CHORUS

ENDING
Reach out your hand and show them that...
You can make a miracle, you can make a miracle, you can make a mi-ra-cle!

IDEAS AND ACTIVITIES for YOU CAN MAKE A MIRACLE

DISCUSSION IDEAS

This song was written for the British Columbia Children's Hospital and their Children's Miracle Network Telethon. *"Whenever I give a concert in a city, I often try to visit the children in the Hospital and sing some of their favourite songs."*

Some children need special help and special treatment to fulfill their dreams. Children's hospitals, through their research, have given families hope that with special treatment their children will get better and lead happy lives. Wheel chairs, personalized Touch Talkers or Inter-talkers, education and therapy allow many children to join in and become an important part of their community.

Do you know someone who has been in a Children's Hospital? Have you ever been in the hospital?

We all make miracles every day when we do things for others.

ACTIVITIES

Learn the sign language for the Chorus and sing this song for a Family Day.

← ROBBIE →

Do something special for the Children's Hospital or Children's Ward in your community. Draw Hug Bugs to decorate the walls or hang over the children's beds. Arrange to visit the hospital to sing, do a magic trick or tell a funny story. Take part in fund raising for your local hospital. Every little bit helps!

Other Songs about Caring
"May There Always be Sunshine",
"Donne-moi la main", "The Hug Bug",
"Everyday Angel", "Wounded Bird",
and "This Little Light of Mine".

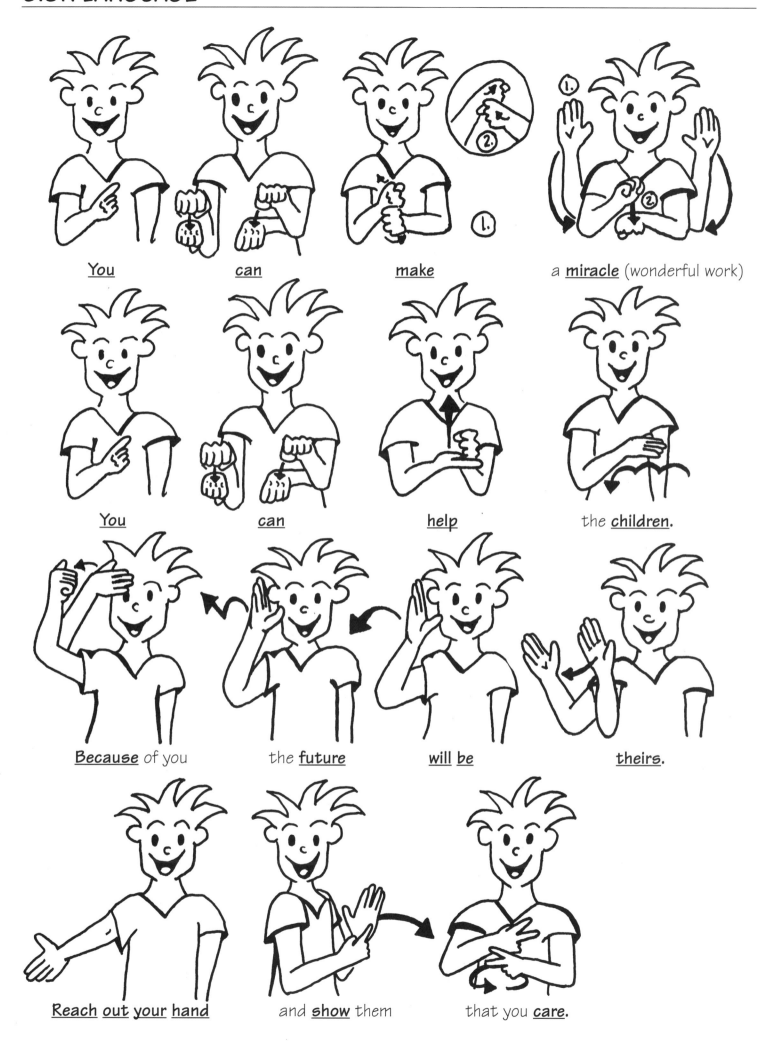

You   can   make   a **miracle** (wonderful work)

You   can   help   the **children**.

Because of you   the **future**   **will** **be**   **theirs**.

Reach **out** **your** **hand**   and **show** them   that you **care**.

DONNE-MOI LA MAIN
(Give Me Your Hand)

By: Guy Auger
Translated to English and Spanish by Charlotte Diamond

Don - ne moi la main, give me your hand,

Don - ne don - ne don - ne donne, don - ne moi la

main.
2. If you're

1. J'ai un a - mi à qui je dis,
ev - er a - lone and feel - ing sad,

Credits: By Guy Auger © Les Éditions du Pollen 1984 SOCAN English Translation by C. Diamond 1986 SOCAN
As recorded on "Diamond in the Rough" and "Qu'il y ait toujours le soleil"

Refrain:
Donne-moi la main
Give me your hand
Donne, donne, donne, donne
Donne-moi la main.

1.
J'ai un ami (une amie) à qui je dis
Toutes mes pensées
Il (elle) prend le temps de s'arrêter
Le temps de m'aider. **Refrain**

2.
Quand tu es seul, quand tu t'ennuies
Viens me visiter
Et à mon tour comme un ami (une amie)
Je vais t'écouter. **Refrain**

English Lyrics - GIVE ME YOUR HAND

English translation by Charlotte Diamond
Original song in French by Guy Auger

CHORUS
Give me your hand, give me your hand
Give to me, please give to me
Give me your hand.

1.
I have a friend with whom I share
All my thoughts and schemes
He takes the time to be my friend
And listen to my dreams.

2.
If you're alone and feeling sad
You can count on me
I'll take the time to help you through
That's how a friend should be.

TOMA MI MANO

Spanish version of "Donne-moi la main" by Guy Auger
Translated to Spanish by Charlotte Diamond
1994 SOCAN
As recorded on "Soy Una Pizza"

Coro
Toma mi mano
Toma mi mano
Toma, toma, tómala
Toma mi mano

1.
Tengo un amigo a quien confiar
Todos mis secretos
El toma el tiempo para escuchar
Y para ayudar
Coro

2.
Si estás solo y muy triste
Ven a visitarme
Yo seré también tu amigo
Y te escucharé.
Coro

IDEAS AND ACTIVITIES for DONNE-MOI LA MAIN

DISCUSSION IDEAS

✌ This song is a great way to begin and end each day. Sit in a circle and join hands while singing.

✌ Why do we feel better when we are in a group? Welcome visitors and new children to your classroom by inviting them to join the circle. Go around the circle and ask everyone to say her name and tell something about herself. **The circle is a wonderful place to communicate with everyone at one time.** Pass around a "talking stick" so that it is clear who is speaking while the rest of the group listens.

ACTIVITIES

✌ Learn the song in French, English or Spanish

✌ Form a circle and join hands. Do the following steps for the Chorus (Refrain).
   - Walk four steps forward - "Donne-moi la main"
   - Walk four steps backward - "Give me your hand"
   - Walk four steps forward (hands raised) - "Donne, donne, donne, donne"
   - Walk four steps backward (hands lowered) - "Donne-moi la main"
   - Walk around in a circle holding hands for the verses.

✌ Try to lift somebody or something by yourself. Then join hands with a partner and try lifting the person or object. Try lifting with four people (in pairs, holding hands or wrists).Try lifting someone with eight people (in pairs, holding wrists).Then slowly rock the person down to the floor. He should have his eyes closed and lay on his back on the joined arms. He may feel like he is floating. This is a lesson in trust and cooperation..

✌ Make patterns in the air with a ribbon stick or scarf in rhythm to the music. See Activities for "La Bamba".

✌ Using a parachute, slowly raise your hands up and down to the music. Take turns being under the parachute.

Other Friendship Songs
"My Bear Gruff", "Find your Spot",
"Cooperation", "Two Books",
"Bats ta pâte" (Making Bread).

ZULU CAROL

Traditional South African Carol
Adapted by: Charlotte Diamond
Arranged by: Paul Gitlitz

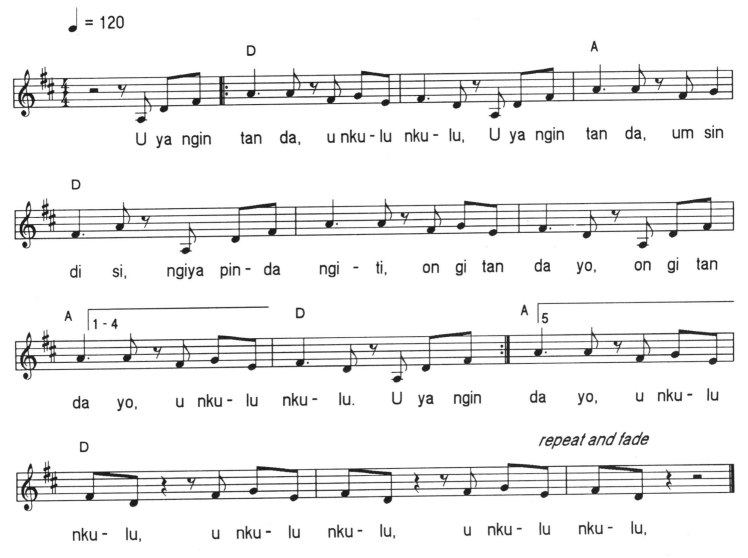

𝅘𝅥 = 120

U ya ngin tan da, u nku-lu nku-lu, U ya ngin tan da, um sin

di si, ngiya pin-da ngi-ti, on gi tan da yo, on gi tan

da yo, u nku-lu nku-lu. U ya ngin da yo, u nku-lu

nku-lu, u nku-lu nku-lu, u nku-lu nku-lu,

repeat and fade

Credits: A traditional South African Carol, in Zulu
Adapted and Arranged by Charlotte Diamond and Paul Gitlitz SOCAN 1990
As recorded on "The Christmas Gift"

u ya ngin tan da
u nkulu u nkulu
u ya ngin tan da
um sin di si
ngiya pinda ngiti
on gi tan da yo
on gi tan da yo
u nkulu u nkulu.

I am loved
by the Almighty
who loves me
the healing is
I say again
that I am loved
and I love
the Almighty.

IDEAS AND ACTIVITIES for ZULU CAROL

DISCUSSION IDEAS

- The "Zulu Carol" is a song of celebration from South Africa. It is an echo song and can be sung by one person leading and a group echoing or two groups (Lead and Echo).

- Chanting or singing together in rhythm can make any job easier, for example, "I've Been Working on the Railroad". Many cultures of our world use echo songs as Work Songs. It is a way to call out instructions and keep in rhythm. This style of singing is also popular in Gospel music.

- Do you know some other songs from Africa? Are they sung in Zulu or another language? Our music in North America has been influenced greatly by African music.

ACTIVITIES

- Find South Africa on a map or globe. What is the weather like there? How do people dress to suit the weather? What does the countryside look like? What animals live there?

- Let's take an imaginary trip to South Africa. Draw a picture of children and their families singing the "Zulu Carol".

- This song is great for playing rhythm instruments as you sing. Start with a few instruments then add more. One group of instruments can echo another.

> ### Other Echo or Work Songs
> "Bats ta pâte (Baking Bread), "V'là le bon vent" (a Voyageur paddling song), "The Days of the Week", "The Banana Boat Song" (Day-o), "All the Nations like Banana", "Michael, Row the Boat Ashore", "Kumbaya"

IDEAS AND ACTIVITIES for DICKY, DICKY DINOSAUR

DISCUSSION IDEAS

- "Dicky Dinosaur" is a rap song about a Stegosaurus. She is a "hip-hoppin' herbivore" who loves to dance.

- Name and describe all the dinosaurs that you know. Which dinosaurs are herbivores (vegetarians) or carnivores (meat eaters)? Did Tyrannosaurus Rex really live at the same time as Stegosaurus?

- Dinosaurs are which type of animal: Amphibians, Reptiles or Mammals? We are not certain if they were warm-blooded or cold-blooded. They laid eggs. Did they build nests and take care of their babies? Which animals on earth are thought to be the descendants of the dinosaurs? Why did the dinosaurs disappear from earth?

ACTIVITIES

- Get out your dark glasses and make up your own "Rap" moves for "Dicky, Dicky Dinosaur". Work with a partner, then share your ideas with the group. *You can see my "Rap" moves in my video "Diamonds and Dragons".*

- Play rhythm instruments. Create sounds with your mouth or by clapping and tapping parts of your body (hambone style).

- Write your own Rap songs. Here is an example of a variation for "Dicky Dinosaur" sent from Ms. Amchin's class in Big Flats, NY.
  Dicky, Dicky Dinosaur is really green
  Dicky, Dicky Dinosaur eats string beans
  Dicky, Dicky Dinosaur is very mean to
  Other dinosaurs who take her beans!
  CHOMP!

> ### Other Songs about Interesting Animals
> "Dragons and Dinosaurs", "Fly High Unicorn", "I'm Being Eaten by a Boa Constrictor", "Slimy the Slug", "Sasquatch", "Animals Have Personality".

- Learn to sing this song in French or Spanish

DICKY, DICKY, DINOSAUR

By: Charlotte Diamond

Dicky, Dicky Dinosaur lives in a swamp
Dicky, Dicky Dinosaur gets very damp
Dicky, Dicky Dinosaur is really neat
But she always trips on her great big feet.
THUD! THUD!

Dicky, Dicky Dinosaur has four legs
Dicky, Dicky Dinosaur lays big eggs
Dicky, Dicky Dinosaur always wails
When you step on the tip of her great long tail
THUD! YIPES!

Dicky, Dicky Dinosaur is lots of fun
Dicky, Dicky Dinosaur loves to run
Dicky, Dicky Dinosaur runs real fast
When Tyrannosaurus Rex is on her path
THUD! YIPES! RUN!

Dicky, Dicky Dinosaur is a friend of mine
Dicky, Dicky Dinosaur has spikes on her spine
Dicky, Dicky Dinosaur loves to roar
But really, she's a gentle Herbivore.
THUD! YIPES! RUN! ROAR!

Credits: By Charlotte Diamond, as recorded on "Diamonds and Dragons"
© Charlotte Diamond Music 1988 SOCAN

DI, DINOSAURIO

Spanish version of "Dicky, Dicky Dinosaur"
by Charlotte Diamond
© Charlotte Diamond Music 1988 SOCAN
As recorded on "Soy una Pizza"

Di, Dinosaurio vive en el pantano
Di, Dinosaurio está muy mojado
Di, Dinosaurio es elegante
Pero es más torpe que un elefante...BUM!!

Di, Dinosaurio pone huevos grandes
Di, Dinosaurio tiene pies gigantes
Di, Dinosaurio se vuelve feroz
Si alguien pisa su cola veloz...BUM!! AY!!

Di, Dinosaurio es un stegosaurio
Di, Dinosaurio le gusta correr
Di, Dinosaurio corre muy rápido
Si Tiranosaurio lo quiere comer...BUM!! AY!!
CORRE!!

Di, Dinosaurio es una bella bestia
Di, Dinosaurio tiene piel eriza
Di, Dinosaurio le gusta rugir
Pero es herbívoro y muy gentil...BUM!! AY!!
CORRE!! GRRRRR!!

DI, DI DINOSAURE

French version of "Dicky, Dicky Dinosaur"
By Charlotte Diamond
© Charlotte Diamond Music 1988 SOCAN

Di, Di Dinosaure habite un marais
Di, Di Dinosaure est toute mouillée
Di, Di Dinosaure est très mignonne
Mais sur ses pattes toujours elle tombe. BOUM!

Di, Di Dinosaure est très heureuse
Di, Di Dinosaure ponde des oeufs
Di, Di Dinosaure est furieuse
Si tu marche sur sa longue queue. BOUM! AIE!

Di, Di Dinosaure est très sportive
Di, Di Dinosaure aime courrir
Di, Di Dinosaure crie, "Courrez"!
Quand Tyrannosaure Rex lui court après. BOUM! AIE!
COURREZ!

Di, Di Dinosaure est très fine
Di, Di Dinosaure porte des épines
Di, Di Dinosaure crie très fort
Mais, c'est un gentil herbivore! BOUM! AIE!
COURREZ! RAR!

10 CRUNCHY CARROTS

By: Charlotte Diamond

10 crunchy carrots, all yours and mine
My gerbils ate one and now there's just 9

9 crunchy carrots, let's bake them in a cake
Sasquatch ate one and now there's just 8

8 crunchy carrots, delicious to munch
Your hamster ate one now there's 7 in the bunch

7 crunchy carrots, let's make some sticks
My sister ate one and now there's just 6

6 crunchy carrots, sweet as honey from the hive
The bees ate one and now there's just 5

5 crunchy carrots, a scratch at the door
The imp wants one and now there's just 4

4 crunchy carrots, a treat for you and me
But the worms ate one and now there's just 3

3 crunchy carrots, what can we do?
Your brother took one and now there's just 2

2 crunchy carrots, a knock at the door
Dracula wants one now there's just one more

1 crunchy carrot, broken in two
Gives a piece for me and a piece for you. Crunch!!
Mm, mm, mm, mm!   Crunch!!   Delicious!!

Credits: By Charlotte Diamond As recorded on "10 Carrot Diamond"
              © Charlotte Diamond Music SOCAN 1985

IDEAS AND ACTIVITIES for 10 CRUNCHY CARROTS

DISCUSSION IDEAS

✍ What is your favourite crunchy vegetable? Why are raw vegetables a great snack? Carrots are a root like turnips, beets and parsnips. The root stores food during the winter to help the plant grow in spring.

✍ Carrots are a **biennial** plant - a plant that lives for two years. A carrot plant does not make seeds until the second year. Some plants are **annuals** and live only one year (tomatoes and peppers), other plants are **perennials** and live for many years (chives, parsley and most herbs).

✍ We eat different parts of plants. For example, a potato and a yam are tubers (roots), celery and asparagus are **stems**, lettuce and cabbage are **leaves**, tomatoes or peppers are fruit and we eat the **seeds** of sunflowers and corn.

ACTIVITIES

✍ Your fingers can be the ten crunchy carrots. Swing them from side to side in rhythm with the music.
Make the fingers disappear as you count down from 10 to 1. (For younger children, start with five carrots.)

✍ Use real carrots or carrot sticks at snack time. Call a child's name as she or he takes a carrot. The last carrot is shared between two children. Why is it important to share?

✍ Let's make musical "crunches". Does the crunch of a celery stick sound like a carrot crunch?

✍ Can you count backwards in different languages. (In French - dix, neuf, huit, sept, six, cinq, quatre, trois, deux, une délicieuse carotte!)

✍ Line up ten raisins and count backwards as you eat them. (They are "chewy" instead of "crunchy")

✍ Grow some carrots from seeds and sing the "Garden Song".
"Inch by Inch, row by row,
gonna make my carrots grow".

✍ Make your own "Big Book" of the "10 Crunchy Carrot Count Down".

Other Counting Songs
"Five Little Sparrows", "Four Hugs a Day", and the folk song "This Old Man".

THE P.R.I.Z.E. METHOD of teaching Songs and Chants

Developed by Charlotte Diamond   © Charlotte Diamond Music 1992
6251 Chatsworth Road, Richmond, B.C. CANADA   V7C 3S4   (604) 274-8216

HERE ARE A FEW TIPS ON WAYS TO HAVE FUN AND LEARN WITH MUSIC.
IT IS SURPRIZINGLY EASY! "THE SONG IS JUST THE BEGINNING."

P. PROPS, PUPPETS & DRAMA - make the words come alive visually

R. RHYTHM and MOVEMENT - find the beat and move to it

I.   IMAGINATION - stimulate creativity, a sense of wonder and discovery

Z. ZIPPER SONGS - write new songs by adding variations to those you know

E. ECHO - CALL AND RESPONSE - the easiest way to teach a song

PROPS, PUPPETS AND DRAMA
- Props enhance the visual impact, add a sense of fun and comedy, reduce the inhibitions of the teacher and the children and increase comprehension of the words.
- A felt board with felt figures or stick puppets with paper figures can animate a story or song. For example, a Slippery fish is eaten by an Octopus, who is eaten by a Tuna Fish, who is eaten by a Great White Shark...etc.
- Puppets allow the focus to pass to a puppet, teddy bear or cuddly toy who can present a different point of view. Puppets encourage conversation and problem solving.
- Drama encourages children to enter into the world of fantasy and imagination through simple costumes: hats, dark glasses, boots, umbrella, a laundry basket, cape and binoculars, dog ears, slug antennae, face paint, or by using different voices, like Dracula.
- Suggested songs: "I Wanna Be a Dog", "Dicky Dinosaur", "Slimy the Slug", "The Hug Bug", "Looking for Dracula", "The Laundry Monster" and "My Bear Gruff", "Puddles", "Octopus".

RHYTHM
- Children love rhythm; it makes the lyrics of a song or chant easier to learn and to remember.
- Hand claps, finger snaps and sound effects help to develop a sense of rhythm.
- Body movement in rhythm encourages physical or kinesthetic involvement with the song, for example sign language or gesture, simple dance, and clapping with a partner.
- Ribbons and scarves follow the flow of the music and allow a child to explore the space around her and create shapes within that area.
- Songs that come from other lands or cultures are easier to teach when we start with the rhythmic pulse of the music. Make simple percussion instruments based on authentic instruments, such as maracas, claves, guiro and tambourine.
- Suggested rhythmic songs - "La Bamba", "Stop and Listen", "Co-operation", "Rubber Blubber Whale", "Zulu Carol", "All the Nations Like Banana", "Bats ta pâte", "The Carousel" and "Hush Little Baby".

MOVEMENT, GESTURE AND SIGN LANGUAGE
- Rhythmic movement unifies the group. Holding hands in a circle is a wonderful way to start and end the day. Working with a parachute also builds a sense of unity.
- Movement increases attention span and participation. When a movement crosses the body midline, both sides of the brain become involved.
- Suggested songs: "Four Hugs a Day", "May There Always Be Sunshine" and "Spider's Web" (in sign language), "Each of Us Is a Flower", "Dicky Dinosaur", "What Kind of Tree are You", "Octopus", "Sing in the Spring", "5 Little Sparrows", "Listen to the Water","De Colores", "Roots and Wings", "Find Your Spot", "Morningtown Ride", "Sh! Sh! Fingers", "Lucky Streak".
- Encourage the children to create their own movements, then share with the group.

IMAGINATION
- The magic words, "Let's pretend" always evoke a sense of mystery, suspense and discovery. Use music to stimulate a child's creative development through word-play and role-play. A very rainy day, a special event, classroom news, such as a new puppy can lead into song or story. Be spontaneous when children have a keen interest in a topic.
- Draw while listening to music. A song can create a mood or expand on a theme.
- Suggested songs and stories: - "Looking For Dracula", "Two Books", "Fly High Unicorn", " Spider's Web", "The Carousel & My Favourite Things", "Dragons and Dinosaurs", "Goodnight Mistress Moon", "I Wanna Be a Dog".

ZIPPER SONGS
- Encourage children to compose their own songs by adapting songs they already know. For example: "I am a Pizza" could become "I am a Sandwich" or "I am a Taco".
- Take the pattern of "My Bear Gruff and add on other animals whose names end in "uff" - Puff, Fluff, Tuff and Ruff. Change "I Wanna be a Dog" to a Bear or a Whale.
- "May There Always Be Sunshine" - change to: May there always be eagles, whales, rhinos or other endangered species.
- Suggested zipper songs: "Listen to the Water" , "It's a Rainy Day", "Sing in the Spring", "Sh! Sh! Fingers" and "What Kind of Tree Are You?" (The Ontario Board of Education wrote a version for the schools called, "What Kind of Fish Are You?")

ECHO SONGS (CALL AND RESPONSE)
- Echoing is one of the most effective ways of teaching lyrics and melody.
- The group can be divided in two, one group leads and the other echoes.
- Echoing is excellent for teaching English as a Second Language, or introducing another language. The teacher can hear more clearly the response of individual children. The children can see how the teacher forms the words, then imitate mouth shape as well as sound.
- Suggested Echo Songs: "I am a Pizza" (Je suis une Pizza) (Soy una Pizza), "Puddles", "Sasquatch", "Looking for Dracula", "The Days of the Week", "The Zulu Carol" and "The Keeper Would a-Hunting Go".

ADDITIONAL SUGGESTIONS

QUIET, SLOWER SONGS FOR THOUGHTFUL MOMENTS
- The use of waltz time - 3/4 or 6/8 and simple lyrics creates a quiet, relaxed mood.
- Sign language is easily integrated when the pace is slower.
- Suggested songs: "Fly High Unicorn", "Donne-moi la main - Give Me Your Hand", "My Bear Gruff", "The Carousel & My FavouriteThings", "The Giving Tree", "Spider's Web","You Can Make a Miracle", "You Never Praise Me Enough", "Wounded Bird","One Dream" and "Everyday Angel",

GOOD FEELINGS
- Several of my songs were written to help build good self-esteem. With so many changes in family structure, children need to feel secure and proud of who they are. They also need to learn how to communicate their feelings and how to treat each other.
- Suggested songs:"Love Me For Who I Am", "Why Did I Have to Have a Sister?", "Lucky Streak", "Four Hugs a Day", "Each of Us Is a Flower", "The Hug Bug", "Everyday Angel", and "When I First Came to This Land".

PLEASE READ TO ME
- Many songs exist as books - " The Foolish Frog", "My Favourite Things ", "De Colores", "The Huron Carol" and "Inch by Inch - The Garden Song".
- Many songs can be read aloud as poetry or stories, such as "Two Books on the Library Shelf", "Dragons and Dinosaurs", "The Toy at the Bottom of the Stocking", and "The Wisest Old Woman and Man". Encourage the children to illustrate the story.

The Heart of a Child

The heart of a child is a tremendous thing
Lovely and frail as a butterfly's wing
Kissed by the beam of a summer sun
Or crushed by the word of a careless one
A look or a smile will cause it to sing
For the heart of a child is a tremendous thing.

(Given to me by Eileen Cole, Red Deer, Alberta)
Author unknown

BIBLIOGRAPHY

Random House Webster's American Sign Language Dictionary 1998 By Elaine Costello
Signing - How to Speak with your Hands, Bantam 1988 By Elaine Costello
Play Power, Games and Activities for Young Children 1994   ISBN 1-885650-00-0 By Sharron Werlin Krull and Norma Don
The Mailbox - The Idea Magazine for Teachers - Kindergarten - June/July 1998 Article by Mackie Rhodes, Page 38.
   1-800-627-8579
The Singing Reading Connection with Shirley Handy National Educational Network 1-800-537-6647

COMPANION BOOKS - Reading and Singing go so well together!

FOUR HUGS A DAY AND THE HUG BUG
Ross, Dave *A Book of Hugs* Thomas Y. Crowell, New York 1980
Simpson, Lesley *The Hug* Annikins, Annick Press, Toronto 1985
Hoban, Russel *Nothing To Do* Harper 1964
Eastman, P.D. *Sam and the Firefly* Beginner Books Random House 1958

MY BEAR GRUFF
Kraus, Robert *Leo, the Late Bloomer* Windmill Books 1971
Boynton, Martin *Why Do You Love Me?* Greenwillow Books 1988
Cohen, Miriam *Will I Have a Friend?* Macmillian 1967
Wise Brown, Margaret *Runaway Bunny* Harper Trophy
Joly, Fanny *Mr. Fine Porcupine* Chronicle
Zolotow, Charlotte *A Tiger Called Thomas* Lothrop, Lee & Shepard 1963

SASQUATCH
Sendak, Maurice *Where the Wild Things Are* Scholastic
Hutchins, Hazel J. *Leanna Builds a Genie Trap* Annick Press

PUDDLES (AND WEATHER)
Lawson, Julie *Midnight in the Mountains* Orca Book Publisher 1998
Schmidt, Eleanore *The Water's Journey* North-South Books
McPhail, David *The Puddle* Farrar, Straus, Giroux
London, Jonathan *Puddles* Viking 1997
Kleven, Elisa *The Puddle Pail* Dutton 1997

SPIDER'S WEB
Kiri, David *Miss Spider's Wedding* Scholastic
Winer, Yvonne *Spiders Spin Webs* Charlesbridge
Carle, Eric *The Very Busy Spider* and *The Very Quiet Cricket* Philomel
Palazzo-Craig, Janet *Why Spider Spins Tales (A story from Africa)* Troll 1996
McNulty, Faith *The Lady and the Spider* Harper 1986

OCTOPUS
Jones, Rebecca *Down at the Bottom of the Deep Dark Sea* Bradbury Press 1991
Schmidt, Eleanore *The Water's Journey* North-South Books
Fernandes, Eugenie *Waves in the Bathtub* Toronto: Scholastic Canada 1993
Pfister, Marcus *Rainbow Fish* North-South Books 1992
Palmer, Helen *A Fish out of Water* Dr. Suess - Random House
Silverstein, Shel *I'm Being Eaten by a Boa Constrictor* Harper Collins
Hickman, Pamela *Hungry Animals* Kids Can
Kasza, Keiko *When the Elephant Walks* Putnam
McFarlane, Sheryl *Jessie's Island* Orca Book Publishers 1992

METAMORPHOSIS
Lobel, Arnold *Frog and Toad are Friends* Harper Collins 1970
Bornstein, Ruth *Little Gorilla* Houghton Mifflin
Carle, Eric *A Very Hungry Caterpillar* Philomel
Hickman, Pamela *A New Butterfly* Kids Can
Ryder, Joanne *Where Butterflies Grow* Lodestar Books 1989
Seeger, Charles and Pete *The Foolish Frog* (Check your library)
Mayer, Mercer *When I Get Bigger* Western Publishers
Miller, Ruth *I Went to the Bay* Kids Can Press 1998

THE DAYS OF THE WEEK (AND SEASONS)
Carle, Eric *Today is Monday* Putnam
Gibbons, Gail *The Seasons in Arnold's Apple Tree* HBJ 1984
Croll, Carolyn *The Little Snowgirl* Putnam 1989
Repchuk, Caroline *The Snow Tree* Templar Books, Great Britain 1996
Ward, Cindy *Cookie's Week* Putnam 1988

> **There are wonderful "Big Books"(Song Cards 11" by 17") for many of my songs available through:**
>
> **Bubble Rock**
> **P.O. Box 3654**
> **Rancho Palos Verdes CA 90275**
> **(310) 541-5819**
>
> **National Educational Network**
> **Hilmar, CA 95324**
> **(209) 668-4142**
> **1-800-537-6647**

MAY THERE ALWAYS BE SUNSHINE
Eastman, P.D. *Are You My Mother ? Eres tu mi mama?* Beginner Books - Random House
   Translated to Spanish by Carlos Rivera
de Paola, Tomie *Nana Upstairs, Nana Downstairs* Putnam 1973
MacLachlan, Patricia *Through Grandpa's Eyes* Harper & Row 1983
Munch, Robert *I'll Love You Forever* Annick
Gilman, Phoebe *Grandma and the Pirates* Scholastic
Miles, Victoria *Sea Otter Pup* Orca Book Publishers 1993

EVERYDAY ANGEL
Cowan-Fletcher, Jane *It Takes a Village* Scholastic 1994
Lionni, Leo *Alexander and the Wind-up Mouse* Pantheon Books, Random House 1969
Guthrie, Donna *A Rose For Abby* Abingdon Press 1988
Wittman, Sally *A Special Trade* Harper Trophy 1978
Fox, Mem *Wilfrid Gordon Macdonald Partridge* Kane/Miller

EACH OF US IS A FLOWER (AND NATURE)
Carle, Eric *The Tiny Seed* Simon and Schuster 1987
Lobel, Arnold *A Rose in My Garden* Scholastic 1984
Carlstrom, Nancy *Wild, Wild Sunflower Child Anna* Macmillian 1987
Mallett, David *Inch by Inch - The Garden Song* Harper Collins
Stewart, Sarah *The Gardener* Farrar Strauss and Giroux
Wilkes, Angela *Growing Things* Highgate Press (Usborne)
Silverstein, Shel *The Giving Tree* Harper Collins 1964
Willow, Diane *At Home in the Rainforest* Charlesbridge 1991

I AM A PIZZA
Prelutsky, Jack *Pizza the Size of the Sun* Greenwillow
Steig, William *Pete's a Pizza* Harper Collins

ALL I REALLY WANT IS PEACE (TOUT CE QUE JE VEUX - LA PAIX)
UNICEF *Children Just Like Me* United Nations Children's Fund Fenn
Hamanaka, Sheila *Peace Crane* Morrow
Hughes, Monica *A Handful of Seeds* UNICEF, Canada Lester Publishing 1993
Moore Thomas, Shelley *Somewhere Today - A Book of Peace* Albert Whitman 1998

LUCKY STREAK
Ziefert, Harriet *A New Coat For Anna* Alfred A Knopf 1986
Williams, Vera *Lucky Song* Greenwillow
Rodgers & Hammerstein/Warhola *My Favorite Things* Simon & Schuster
Viorst, Judith *Alexander and the Terrible, Horrible, No Good Day* Aladdin

ONE DREAM
King, Martin Luther *I Have a Dream* Scholastic
Heyer, Marilee *Weaving a Dream* Penguin Books 1989
Everett, Louise *Amigo Means Friend* Troll Books 1987
Hamanaka, Sheila *All the Colors of the Earth* William Morrow 1994

YOU CAN MAKE A MIRACLE
Dr Suess *Horton Hatches the Egg* Random House
Davison, Martine *Maggie and the Emergency Room* Developed by the American
  Medical Association Random House
Rosenberg, Maxine B. *My Friend Leslie* Lothrop, Lee & Shepard
Cohen, Miriam *It's George* Greenwillow

DONNE-MOI LA MAIN (GIVE ME YOUR HAND)
Marino, Susan *Friends Forever* Modern Publishers 1989
Cohen, Miriam *Best Friends* McMillain 1971

ZULU CAROL
Isadora, Rachel *A South African Night* Greenwillow
Mennen, Ingrid & Daly *Somewhere in Africa* Dutton 1990

10 CRUNCHY CARROTS
Kraus, Ruth *The Carrot Seed* Harper & Row 1945
Vagin, Vladimir *The Enormous Carrot* Scholastic
Murphy, Stuart Math Start: Comparing Amounts *Just Enough Carrots* Scholastic 1997

DICKY, DICKY DINOSAUR
Schnetzler, Pattie *Ten Little Dinosaurs* Accord
Mayer, Marianna *The Unicorn and the Lake* Dial Books 1982
Sweat, Lynn & Philips, Louis *The Smallest Stegosaurus* Penguin

Suggested Sources for Charlotte Diamond's Recordings, Videos and Songbook (Check these sources or your Public Library for the Companion Books as well.)

CANADA
Kidsbooks (Vancouver, B.C.) and Kidsbooks at the Village (North Vancouver)
(604)738-5335 (604) 986-6190 or 1-800-893-5335
Children's Bookstore (Toronto, Ontario)
(416) 480-0233 1-800-265-5622
2532 Yonge St. Toronto, ON M4P 2H7
Scholar's Choice Moyers
(London, Ontario) 1-800-265-1095

UNITED STATES
The Linden Tree Bookstore (Los Altos, CA)
(650) 949-3390
All For Kids (Seattle, WA) (206) 526-2768
Bubble Rock (see pg 87)
National Educational Network (see pg 87)
Rounder Kids (Roundup Records)
(Cambridge, MA) 1-800-443-4727
Educational Record Centre
(Wilmington, NC) 1-800-438-1637

FOR FURTHER INFORMATION CONTACT:
Hug Bug Music Sales & Distribution
(604) 931-7375 Fax: (604) 931-2727
or E-mail: hugbug@intergate.bc.ca

For Concerts, Workshops and Keynote Presentations, please call:
Hug Bug Music Bookings (604) 274-8216
Fax: (604) 274-8210 or
E-mail: hugbug@intergate.bc.ca
Please send Charlotte your suggestions of other books that you would recommend that compliment the themes of her songs.